A Special Thank You

This book was self-published by me and my friends, including everyone who supported our Kickstarter campaign. While I wrote it, my community made it happen. If you're ever curious about self-publishing I suggest you try it. There is something intrinsic about working with a community to make something creative happen. I'd be willing to argue it might be the future of publishing. Just a thought.

This is a list of our Critical Mass Backers, those who elected to give considerably to our Kickstarter campaign. This space in the book is dedicated specifically to them. Friends and family, your generosity speaks volumes about your character. Thank you for believing.

Dad & Mom

Grandpa Dwight & Grandma Joan Green

Uncle Jack & Aunt Dena Morehouse

Andrew Morehouse

Ashley Reiman

Bryan Dormaier

Aaron Delani

Jason Proctor

WE
WERE
LIKE
SONS

A MEMOIR BY AARON M. GREEN

An Illocution Studio Book
Portland, Oregon

An Illocution Studio Book
Copyright © 2015 by Aaron M. Green

Published in Portland, Oregon, by Illocution Studio.

Library of Congress Cataloging-in-Publication Data

We Were Like Sons / Aaron M. Green
ISBN: 978-0-9962692-0-9
Library of Congress Control Number: 2015906017

Interior design by Aaron Delani
Cover design by Tyler Madsen
Cover image by Aaron Delani

www.illocution.us
www.wewerelikesons.com

For Les, Jared, Tyler & Eric

Back in those days when I may have cornered you in too many rooms
to complain about too many hard things going on,
you never tried to inch toward the doors.
Instead, you picked me up and took me on adventures.
I'll marvel at that forever.

To you I dedicate this book.

Contents

Part I.

Part II.

Part III.

Part IV.

Part V.

Preface

In preparing to self-publish this book, I looked through a dozen of my favorite books and was baffled to find that they had prefaces I'd never read. I'd skipped right over them, much as I tend to skip over forewords and introductions. I'm the type of reader that likes to cut right to the chase. Just drop me into the story already, I don't have time for a setup!

So, if you're anything like me, you've likely arrived on this page only after you've finished reading the book. High-five! But, wherever you are, it may be helpful to know a couple things to help make sense of it.

First, if I learned anything by reading those dozen or so prefaces, it was that they set a tone. They left an impression, in the same way that I hope to leave one with you as you go on to read (and hopefully reread). I'd like to think of it as if we're meeting for the first time at a party, sharing about our lives and joking a bit, and giving each other a hug before exiting from our conversation. I'd want you to know that this book was risky for me to write, and that it took me a long time to finally do it.

Second, I got the impression that a preface might be used to prepare readers for any stylistic or out-of-the-ordinary literary behavior. This way, the reader isn't dropped into a type of world they've never read and might find annoying or distracting. Again, if you're like me, and you don't care about that stuff, then go ahead and skip the next two paragraphs. As we both know, you can always come back to them later!

This book is going to be different than most books you've read. Most books, but not all. I don't mean that to sound snooty or patronizing. When I imagine what I look like when I'm being snooty or patronizing it makes me want to shake my head and bite my lip and then push myself down some stairs.

What I mean by different is that this book takes some literary risks that I'm already sure some folks won't be too humored by. It swings between the past and present tenses and changes from third to first person at the dawning of new chapters. My intent was not to distract or evidence anything to you, my readers, about my (lack of) literary expertise, but to tell two stories simultaneously, in the way some movies follow a single storyline but flash at times into the past to show snapshots of another time or place. My proofreaders assured me at first that this decision sounded risky and bordered on confounding, but after our reading and rereading and rereading, and upon copious and laborious editing, we are now in agreement.

With all sincerity, it is my honor to present to you, We Were Like Sons. I hope you love this book.

—Aaron M. Green
February, 2015

Part I.

Beside Myself

What time is it? This comes first. Early morning light is peaking through his dusty green drapes. The walls have already changed from nighttime blacks and deep blues to dampened yellows and oranges. One eye is open and examining and the other remains closed. He is half covered by a blanket that swells with body warmth. Birds are calling to one another from the telephone wire across the backyard.

Saturday, he thinks. *Today, is Saturday. Wait, what time is it?* He swings his hand across his desk and smacks his phone from the surface. It hits the floor. It's too late, too late in the morning. He retrieves the phone and brings it to his face.

It is 7:45 a.m.

The idea of riding a bicycle across America is plenty for any restless young man's imagination to chew on: summiting hills after long climbs, the sounds of backcountry rivers, the smell of the forest, the Colorado Rockies, wind through unkempt hair, hundreds and hundreds of miles of farmland, hospitality of strangers. To talk about it between making jokes over beers on a Friday night with friends is one thing. But to do it is another.

Aaron avoids the thought of keeping his friends and family patiently waiting. His friend Jared, one among the mass who will be gathered for the send-off ceremony along the Pacific coast, will no doubt say upon his arrival: "There he is—late to his own send-off. Called it." Instead, Aaron is a whirlwind around his bedroom collecting his bags, books and clothes. His soap hits the back of his bag and falls to the bottom; his extra pairs of socks and his coffee press are recklessly crammed wherever they will fit. He pulls into his cycling shorts and jersey and throws open the bedroom door.

"Dad?" he calls out from the doorway.

His dad is outside filling his own bike tires with air. He plans to ride with Aaron and Les as far as he can on day one, giving them his own kind of send-off. From there he'll return home just like everyone else. Nothing is said as Aaron hurls his bags into the back of his dad's pickup and jogs over to his bike to emulate his father's actions.

"Ready to go, Dad?" he asks.

His dad stops pumping and looks as if he's thinking. He shrugs and says, "Yep. Are you?"

This hits Aaron funny. It is at this moment that he realizes how little time he's taken to prepare himself internally. His dad takes up pumping again and Aaron watches his hands rising and falling together as they slowly inflate his tires. They are indicative of his father, somehow representing how his dad has been ready, or at least how he's always known to be ready.

When satisfied with his tire's pressure, the older man's eyes rise and study his driveway, and then he looks to Aaron. Some say a boy doesn't become a man until his father has said so, and even then, that it might take years to realize. Aaron knows this moment is important but can't explain why. He stands next to his Dad on the asphalt driveway, full of dead grass and hundreds of cracks, and takes it in with him.

"Yeah, I guess I am ready," Aaron says.

"Alright," his dad says, wrapping the hose of the bike pump around the metal, cylindrical neck and locking it into place. "Then let's hit the road."

At first, Aaron was skeptical of a send-off ceremony. It felt self-absorbed, and he was suspicious of needing to draw that kind of attention to Les's and his bicycling adventure. Really though, he was hesitant to believe anybody would show up. Still, he and Les invited everybody that they could think of to join in an amalgamation of last words, hugs and prayers.

As the brown pickup hums to a stop a block from the Huntington Beach Pier at 8:15 a.m., Aaron feels his stomach turning. His bags are crammed at his feet, and as he opens the door he sees them fall into the gutter. He exhales and looks toward the ocean. *I guess this is what it feels like to be beside myself.* He watches his movements: his hands stacking camping items upon his rack, pulling cables up and over and snapping them into place, steadying his heavy bike.

FOOD PANTRY POGS

Pogs were a passing fad in the '90s, just like marbles, yo-yos, and Giga Pets. I even remember watching kids play jax at recess when I was in third grade. Jax! I think kids find silly hobbies like these and learn to obsess over them because of some innate desire to fit in, and the younger the kid, the more they seem to care about this. Whether it's something that passes the time or something they go on to excel at, kids are an innocent proof of man's desire to do what it takes to be accepted.

I liked collecting pogs, even more than I liked playing the game of pogs. The game of pogs, as I understood it, didn't make a whole lot of sense. It was between two players who'd stack their pogs in a tower, alternating as they went, followed by each throwing a slammer (a disc similar to the size of a pog but made of heavier plastic rather than cardboard) down at the tower and letting the pogs fall as they would. If you made your opponent's pogs flip over, then you got to keep them. Slammers were where kids could really get to spending their money. For me, however, five dollars for a slammer felt as far away from my reach as buying a car.

The first time I saw pogs was when Henry Martinez brought nine or ten to school in a Ziploc bag. They were bright, glossy and lightweight. I felt as though I was looking at currency the way he kept them safely below the plastic zip lock. They may as well have been gold. Henry brought these to school before anyone knew there was even a game to be played. Soon, like Henry had started the fad himself, kids everywhere were showing up to school with Ziplocs full of them. But from there the pog economy soon grew out of the Ziploc, and kids were showing up with neon, transparent vials called "pogtainers" they'd purchased from Toys "R" Us or a comic book store.

Much like with slammers, I'd walk over to my local comic book store to simply look at the pogtainer vials. They were the latest pog accessory, and they stood on proud display. Pogs themselves were now on the peripheral, and the slammers were one case closer, but right where the eye's sight naturally fell were one and two foot tall, neon-colored vials that pogs could be contained within. I remember looking at them for a while, and as I did I felt something faint and certain inside of me. It wasn't envy or covetousness about not being able to afford a cool neon pogtainer, but a simple realization that one of them wouldn't be mine. I had almost no money, nor any access to it, so this lavish side of pog collecting would never be a corner of the fad that I'd understand.

When I got home from the comic book store that day I had an idea. The holiday season was on us, and someone had given my family something that resembled a pogtainer: a huge plastic candy cane filled with Hershey's Kisses. It wasn't neon, but it was cylindrical, and it was transparent plastic. It had a red plastic hook like the top of a real candy cane that fit onto the cylinder as a cap. Inside, there must have been at least a hundred Kisses.

I went straight to it, popped off the red hook and dumped the wrapped chocolates onto my bed. Then, I took my collection of pogs (only six at the time), and carefully dropped them into the candy cane like slowly loading a rifle from the tip downward into the barrel, watching them slide all the way to the bottom. I held it in the air and saw how it still had three feet of empty space for me to fill. Plenty of potential to collect as many pogs and slammers as I'd like, I thought.

I was then faintly certain of something else, but this time it felt good and right. It was that I was resourceful and that I could learn to pass off things as the real deal without the need for money or privilege. I was sure that I didn't need anyone else, at least not to become the better pog collector that I wanted to be.

With three feet of former Hershey Kiss space, I knew now that I'd need to find a way to fill it. I saw myself going to school with my repurposed pogtainer hanging halfway out of my backpack, kids asking what it was, and then me revealing my collection, unsheathing it like a sword. Though I'd never say this aloud to my friends, in those moments I'd want for them to realize how dinky their plastic, neon pogtainers were in comparison to my resourcefulness.

I knew my vision of becoming the best pog collector at school would take time. Since I knew I couldn't make my own pogs (though I'd considered cutting circles out of cereal boxes), I'd either need to start finding ways to make money to buy pogs, or figure out a way to inherit them.

Fortunately, the latter fell literally into my lap.

My family and I attended one of the largest churches in North Orange County at the time. One of the greatest benefits that megachurches have to offer is their capability to be a resource for those in need. Our church had a rather large food pantry at the time, and families in need could come and pick out food, free of charge. The food in the pantry was made up mostly of donations from other members in the church. If people knew where to look around our ten-acre campus, they'd find inconspicuous grey tubs where they could walk up and drop in their donations whenever they liked.

Unbeknownst to me or any of my siblings at the time, when my mom or dad would pull the family station wagon down the road and into the church parking lot on evenings during the week, this was to utilize the food pantry. It was for grocery shopping. While I perused the store brand mac 'n' cheese and tried on funny-looking coats hanging in a closet—what I thought to be someone's halloween costume—my mom and dad were making sure our family got by.

One evening after finding no interesting costumes in the closet, I was sitting at a foldout table beneath a storage cupboard when a box fell onto the table and spilled its contents, much of it landing right in my lap. I looked around and nobody else seemed to have noticed. On the table I saw party hats, tissue wrapping paper and tape, but into my lap had fallen two half-gallon Ziploc bags full of pogs.

I held each bag up and studied them. I weighed them and noticed many of them were bright and glossy. A food pantry attendant, an older man with glasses and a tucked-in Oxford shirt with an apron over it, came over. Having not been sure what happened, I sat waiting to see if he'd be upset about the box that fell.

"What happened here?" he said.

I didn't move.

"Looks like you almost got crushed," he smiled. I looked at the box and its former contents everywhere. They didn't look as if they could have crushed me. He went on. "Oh yes, and look at these here." He picked up one of the bags of pogs and studied them closely as I had, but with more scrutiny. "Just as I thought. Milk caps."

"Milk caps?" I said.

"That's right, they used to cap milk bottles with paper circles like these. Used to come with the milk company's logo. They died out about the time that there was no longer a need for a milkman, but I'm glad to see they're still around. Kids these days like to collect these, don't they?" He looked over at the other bag, the one that was in my hands. "Seems you might be a collector. Am I right?"

I nodded, not sure what more to say. I felt then a little like an orphan character named Joe from Santa Claus, the Movie—a movie I loved—who'd grown up on the streets and got the chance to hang out with Santa while he finished delivering gifts to children. I remembered Joe having this thing where he never felt deserving of anyone's gifts. But Santa knew just what would make Joe happy. "Just say, 'yo,'" Santa said to Joe after inviting him into the sleigh on the night they met. "Yo?" Joe questioned and off the reindeer went.

"Well, you'd better take these caps then. No sense in keeping them here and letting nobody collect them," the man said.

I looked at him, and for a second I wondered if he might be Santa incarnate.

"Go on," he said, pushing the second bag toward me. I still didn't know what to say. The whole thing felt weird, as if I was being told to take what I wanted from someone's garage by a strange man wearing an apron.

"Okay," I said.

He smiled again and said, "Give them a good home. They're yours."

That night when I got home I filled my candy cane pogtainer with my newly acquired pogs, two by two, and watched them fill all three feet of empty space. When I'd capped it off with the red hook, I let the candy cane and its pogs rest against my bedroom wall. I laid down on my bed, watching and admiring my new collection, and soon fell asleep.

Departure

He pulls in a stomach of air and then lets it out. He mounts his bike, and his dad does the same, and together they ride toward the Huntington Beach Pier for the send-off.

There is a crowd of around forty gathered along the sidewalk under the pier. As he nears he recognizes most of them. He hears a shout come from the far side of the group.

"He's here!"

Heads spin to the sidewalk, and the group cheers. People approach to hug and show their support. The last of the group is Les. The smile on his face is different than everyone else's. It is sly. Aaron returns the expression and says, "We're really going to do this, aren't we?"

Aaron looks around at the group, noticing the way they smile and how they talk, and knows he is surrounded by his people. They are warm, excited and fully supportive.

Departure is close, and he can feel it. On the outside he is smiling, but inside he is realizing he's terrified. His heart rate has quickened; his stomach is knotted and sour. Even breathing seems a task. *I thought I'd be more excited than this,* he thinks.

It was Les's idea to have a tire-dipping ceremony. It was likely something he read on a bike touring blog. In theory Aaron and Les would dip their back tires into the Pacific and then, when they had crossed the country, they would dip their front tires into the Atlantic. As the crowd trudges through the sand toward the ocean, people all around are smiling and laughing. Les comes over to Aaron and whispers that he's never seen a tire-dip, but that they'll just make it up. Side by side they walk their unloaded bikes into ankle-deep waters and then slowly lift their bikes into the air. They pause for pictures and dramatic effect, and while Aaron brings his bike back into the wet sand, Les holds his pose for almost twenty more seconds, at one point holding the bike in one arm and flexing the other. The crowd cheers as waves submerge their legs from below. In unison they count to three, raise their bikes again and dip their rear wheels into the sea. They glance at each other and shrug, and soon everyone is trudging through the sand back toward the sidewalk.

A circle forms at Les's beckoning. Les and Aaron stand in the middle; family members approach, then friends and then acquaintances. Several people begin to pray aloud at the same time and then quickly go quiet, peeking up and looking around to see if they should begin again or let the other prayer continue. The assertive voice of Les's uncle prevails, initiating the group prayer, and others then follow.

With his head down, Aaron thinks about the ride and America's great backyard in his path. A blend of excitement and apprehension courses his body; he is nervous, but he is ready. His adventure is before him, motioning for his crossing. *A call to adventure*, he thinks. *A time to look for God and purpose with new eyes.*

After prayers the group falls mostly silent. "One of us should give a speech," Aaron says to Les, looking over. Les nods looking back.

"Well, alright everyone—" Aaron starts. "I guess, uhh—good-bye." He waves and throws a leg over his bike. Les does the same, along with Aaron's dad and their friend Joe, who would both ride as far out with them on this first day as they could before turning back.

Eastbound for a while, Aaron thinks, pedaling down the boardwalk. "And here we go," he says aloud.

FRIENDS WHO PUSH US

May 2007 — thirteen months until departure

I met Les during the summer of 1997. This was before entering seventh grade, when all eleven- and twelve-year-olds come into junior high with fresh eyes and minds and quickly discover that the next several years will be spent learning all about what it means to be cool. Usually, if they were cool they didn't have to try—they simply were. Les didn't seem to care very much about being cool, and I didn't get the feeling that he thought about it a lot. Rather, he seemed to have more important things to think about, like girls. Of course, this made him really cool. Certainly cooler than me. We probably ended our first encounter with a quick hand-slap-to-fist-bump handshake (a rite of passage among boys in those days to signify coolness) and settled into a small cabin with five other generally awkward preteen boys at our church's junior high summer camp in Big Bear, California.

Les and I went on to spend the next six years in the same church group, but for whatever reason it wasn't until our senior year in high school that we really became friends. Les knew that I played the bass guitar, and one Sunday after church we met for lunch to talk about me joining a band he led. I was excited, of course. I'd already begun practicing with my friends in our indie-rock band, The Jacaranda Jam, and getting the opportunity to play with Les meant jamming and learning alongside him as well. After high school we went to different colleges, but the depth of our church experiences and playing music together seemed to keep us close. Every couple months we'd meet for lunch to catch up, share experiences, philosophize about church and theology, and of course, talk about girls.

Over the years I learned Les was a three-sided person. First, he was an organizational freak. Upon completing Dr. Gary Smalley's "Five-Minute Personality Test," whereby a test taker's results ended in an animal personality, Les learned he was unequivocally a "beaver." According to the test, beavers are organized; they think there is a right way to do everything; they are creative; they like solving. Their strengths are respect, order and high standards. Their weaknesses are unrealistic expectations of themselves and of others and perfectionism. The evening he received his animal designation, Les signed up for a new instant-messaging account, merging his last name with his beaver persona: RorickBeaver. Then he invited one hundred people to chat with him at the same time. (That last part might not be entirely true.)

Second, Les was a spontaneous thrill-seeker—meaning spontaneously he would always be seeking out thrills. Once, while walking through a park and talking with him about something serious, I looked over and he was gone. Confused, I peered in every direction but couldn't find him anywhere. When I finally looked up, I saw that he was twenty feet into a tree and peering down at me, waiting for me to go on with what I was saying. Another time while we were jogging through a different park I saw him suddenly scale an A-frame swing set and tiptoe across the three-inch steel top bar. Also, to this day, Les remains the only person I've ever seen strip naked and ride downhill on his bike at forty miles per hour on a main tourist thoroughfare.

Third, Les was a pastor. His skills applied to people. Anyone who knew him would say his intentionality was beyond comparison, and early on he learned how to lead conversations, mostly through eye contact and without imposing his thoughts before being invited to do so. Because of this, he was often given opportunities to speak logic, love and truth about the ways he saw the world and people working in tandem with God. Les learned that people's hearts were more open only after first getting to release what was troubling them.

When all three pistons were pumping, he was a roaring locomotive of a personality, usually deciding to go to wild places, say bold things and meet people whom nobody had considered meeting. To him, the world was God's and made to be explored. Those of us who knew Les and were willing to follow needed only to smile, nod and get on board.

One evening, nearly ten years after the first day we met, Les, our friend Jared and I were hanging out, sipping coffee on the patio of a coffee shop in Southern California. I was slouched in my chair, mindlessly tossing paper straw wrappings onto the center of the table and spouting off melancholic thoughts and ideas meant simply to hit the breeze in the nighttime air and float away. I was lamenting the loss of the girl I thought I was going to marry. But more on that later.

Eventually, I became self-conscious and worried that I'd sounded too depressing and that my complaints might not be floating away as I'd assumed but piling up on the table in front of my friends. In a sincere attempt to redeem myself, because I hated the idea of inconveniencing them, I offered an idea. My hope was to convey something figurative. A joke. It was to be a statement meant to wipe the table clean of my complaints.

"What if we rode our bikes across the country?" I said, hoping to garner a laugh or at least to diffuse any tension I'd created. I didn't expect any real response, but I sat up in my chair to feign seriousness.

Les stared at the table in front of me for several seconds. Then he looked at my paper straw shards. Then, looking me dead in the eye he said, "Okay. When are we going?"

I laughed. "Good one."

Jared looked up from his book. I glanced over at the used bike I'd just bought. All I knew was that it was called a Shogun and that it was a road-racing bike that was made in the eighties. Tall and quick when it hit the scene two decades ago, it now rested against a wall like an old dog. I wondered if it or I could even make it out of California. I waited for Les to crack, but after several uncomfortable seconds his expression was still the same. I tried to wait him out a few seconds longer. Then I gave in and said, "Oh, dude, you're completely serious aren't you?"

"Of course I am," he said, peering across at me the same way he'd peered down at me from that tree in the park.

Sourness squirmed through my chest. I let out another laugh and looked at Jared for help. He was amused and seemed content holding his finger in his book and waiting to see what would happen next.

"Wait, so come on, man," I said. "This is crazy. We can't actually ride bikes across the country," I said, saying it now as if it was Les's idea. "Can that even be done?"

"Why not?" He said blankly. He was serious. His intention was to call me out. It might have been the past few weeks I'd spent drooping my shoulders and transitioning from mourning to complaining that made him want me to stand up and do something. But I think it was something more, too. I think he made a connection. He saw an opportunity to do something life changing and unique both for himself and to help his friend. Spontaneous thrill-seeker met pastor, and judging by the circumference of his pupils, I could see the organizational freak was already planning.

"Okay," I said and looked down the empty street outside the coffee shop. It felt like I was about to agree to do something insane. I paused and took a deep breath. "How about this time next summer?"

"Done." He snapped his fingers and folded his hands behind his head.

Jared smirked, shook his head and kept reading.

Gestures

Every stroke is the equivalent of being ten feet closer to New York, Aaron thinks. *Ten feet. Twenty feet. Thirty. Forty...*

The four cyclists ride with the gentle push of a tailwind and sail quickly up the Santa Ana river trail. In no time, they are ten miles inland, ten miles further from home and ten miles closer to New York.

When they stop to stretch their legs at a park they find a cyclist with legs like upside-down bowling pins and a bright green jersey that bulges as if it's hiding a large wraparound balloon. He is propped against a tree and wearing sunglasses that are too small for his face. Like some sort of gatekeeper, he watches them vaguely and curiously. At what must have seemed the right moment the man pushes away from the tree and waddles over. Looking up and down at their pannier bags and tightly packed bikes he says, "So what's your story?"

"Just an hour in actually," Aaron starts to say. "Kinda funny." He looks over at his dad and Les. "Well, it's not that funny actually. We're riding to New York."

The man is unaffected. He nods and begins to reel off his own tour stories. "Back in the glory days..." he says, looking across at each of their faces. His arms come together again as when he was leaning against the tree, and while staring up at the sky he tells them about how he has done hundreds of bike trips.

"But none," he indicates with his index finger wagging in the air, "none as long as yours will be."

Aaron swallows slowly and looks at Les again, who is fully entranced by the fat man.

Les hands him a small business card with their blog address on the front and the words "Tour Life" typed on the back.

"Tour life," the man reads aloud, flipping the card over. "We all need a little of that, don't we?" He smiles. "Kudos to you, gentlemen, on your trip. Don't worry, I know you'll do it." With his palms facing upward, as if to scoot them off, he has concluded his own kind of departure ceremony. Aaron interprets his gesture as saying, Good luck. I'll be here when you get back, as will we all. We'll nod to your travel stories when our paths meet again.

They wave and move toward the path.

"Sorry, guys," Joe says suddenly.

"For what?" Aaron says.

Joe is looking at the ground, his face firm and bothered. Aaron can tell he wants to say something, but by Joe's hesitancy understands why he can't get himself to do it. While in conversation about the bike trip over the few weeks leading up to the trip, Joe would smile and sarcastically say that he would ride out with them and probably just keep going. "I'll just pick up camping gear along the way," he'd said. "I'll figure it out; don't even worry about it!" Now that the time has come; however, it is clear that the responsibilities in Joe's life, primarily to his fiancée and to his work, restrict him from going any farther.

"It's time for me to turn back," Joe says.

In a moment of hasty desire for his friend to come along, Aaron feels himself wanting nothing more than for Joe to share in the story of touring America by bicycle. But, like Joe, he says nothing about it. Instead, he nods and says, "Alright, man, no problem. Thanks for getting this far with us. It really means a lot."

Joe wrings the rubber grips on his handlebars. Aaron wishes he could say something more, anything that would make Joe's decision to stay back easier.

"Absolutely, brother," Joe says. "Just wish I could keep going. Really, I do."

"I know you do," Aaron says. The two hug, and Les, Aaron's dad and the fat man leaning against the tree all wave Joe off.

In Corona, Aaron's dad treats them to a fast-food lunch. They joke about the heat, about the irony of eating cheeseburgers on the first day of a bike trip and about running out of water somewhere.

"None of this feels real," Les says, pushing french fries into his mouth and staring out at the parking lot. "Still hasn't set in."

"Kind of feels like we're just out for a ride on any old summer day," Aaron says.

"Thirty-five miles inland. It's the perfect time to head back home," Les jokes.

When they finish eating and push back outside, Aaron's dad is quiet. He loops the strap on his old Bell helmet through its holes and pulls it tight and then looks in the direction they came.

"Well," he says, meeting Aaron's eyes. "We better pray." This isn't a peculiar action. Aaron and his brothers and sister were raised going to church and learning to pray. Still, Aaron is caught off guard by his father's decision to suddenly pray in public.

Les and Aaron step in to listen.

"Well, Lord, protect them, guide them. Thank you for giving us yourself." His dad looks up and says, "Amen."

One thing Aaron's family was not used to doing was showing physical affection, but since his father had taken the first step to pray, Aaron decides to take one of his own. He wraps his arms around his dad for the first time since he was a kid. "Thanks, Dad," he says, "for everything." A rush of unexpected emotion shoots through Aaron's body as he feels his father close his arms around him.

"Yeah," his dad says. "Talk to you later."

Aaron watches his father, like an older version of himself, mount his bike, push down on his pedals and turn back the way they came.

Aaron removes his journal and sits down on a curb outside the restaurant. He attempts to write down everything he is thinking, though his pen doesn't move for a moment but trembles in the air above the page. He knows his mind is full—he is experiencing a unique moment of ideas, emotions, memories—but it isn't until he forces himself to press pen to paper that he starts to put concepts to his feelings:

> *Cherished. Loved. Loveable. Joy. These are what I feel. This man—my dad—has done his part. He has sent his son upon the greatest journey of his life. He has sent him off to become a man.*
>
> *Though it was never a journey I thought I'd take, and while my dad couldn't be here for more than half of the first day, his gesture of riding this far is full of significance. It feels like a symbol; it seems to display, despite however many years that I missed feeling his love, his concern that I know he cares about me. My dad loves me. This feels like the truest thing I've ever known.*

Aaron rereads and then exhales. When he is finished he looks at Les, who is staring out at the street. Aaron shrugs.

"Yeah?" Les says.

"That hug, and his decision to come this far with us," Aaron says. "That just meant so much more to me than anything I've felt in a long time."

Les smiles. "That's a gift, bro."

Aaron doesn't say anything. He looks down the road and wonders how far his dad has gotten. He'd love to see him once more.

"Well, alright. Here we go," Les says, standing. "East we go."

"Yeah," Aaron says. "East."

The Circle of Life

The second half of the day feels nothing like the first. Mostly, it is hotter, but also the wide and open bike path they'd ridden along the Santa Ana River since Huntington Beach had ceased shortly after Aaron's dad turned back. They are forced instead to ride with traffic on main thoroughfares without bike lanes. Occasionally, Les reveals a crumpled car map from his pannier bag to make sure they are still on the right track. Tonight the plan is to stay in Redlands, with the parents of Les's girlfriend, Alice. It is approximately sixty-five miles from where they started, and her family has offered their house for the first night of the tour. When they arrive they find taped to the front door a handwritten sign that reads:

COME ON IN WEARY TRAVELERS!

As they step inside they hear, "Welcome home, guys!" Both look toward the top of the stairway and see a tall man who must be Alice's dad. His arms are wide, and he is smiling. He walks down his stairway two steps at a time to greet them.

"This place is as good as yours as it is mine," he says, grinning and shaking their hands. "I'm Larry," he says to Aaron. "And Les, hey! You made it!" He puts his arm around Les and says, "I want to know everything about the ride so far. The heat, the sights, which route you took." He stops and says, "Oh," motioning toward the second story, "but actually, get settled in. You can drop off all your gear in those guest rooms. We'll have dinner ready in a half hour."

"Thanks, Larry. Really appreciate it," Aaron says.

Larry smiles and gives them a salute and then walks into the kitchen.

As they climb the stairway the smell of spices and pasta sauce is in the air. Les takes the old baby room, and Aaron the spare room to its right. There is a window on the western side that casts a rich golden stream of light across the room. The walls are fresh ivory, and there is a simple twin bed, a dresser and an attached bathroom with a personal shower. Aaron swabs away the day's dirt and sweat in a cloud of steam and pulsing water and wonders how amazing a shower would feel after riding through the Rockies, or after a one-hundred-mile ride through Kansas.

When he is finished he finds Les is already freshly dressed, downstairs and having a conversation with Larry outside.

Aaron takes the opportunity to meet Alice's mother, Janet. She is petite and as energetic as her husband. Her eyes are a blaze of excitement as she rushes him to sit and eat any and every appetizer he can manage.

After a few minutes of ravaging appetizers, a rag hits Aaron in the back of the head. He turns to find Les motioning him outside. "We should clean our bikes before it gets too dark," he says, reaching for another rag. "Larry said these rags will work just fine."

"Oh," Aaron says. He looks at the rag and wonders how dirty his bike has actually become after one day. Looking up at Les, Aaron realizes that he must want to respect Larry's advice. Kind of a pre-son-in-law rite, he figures. He walks outside to join them.

Larry stands by observing, emanating his energy but clearly lost in his head. Like Aaron's dad, it seems, Larry would leave everything to join them on their adventure if he could. This is clear when he starts speaking of his own tour stories and races on his bicycle. He turns to Aaron and mentions that he is a dentist and that he has been for over twenty years. Aaron nods, balancing his eyesight between the spot he is cleaning and Larry. Larry says he's finally reached a point in his life where he can take time to race, ride and have adventures again. "This is, in a way, the circle of life," he says smiling.

For dinner they feast on spaghetti and homemade meatballs with garlic bread, salad and wine. Afterward, they swap stories and enjoy ice cream on the patio. This Redlands summer night atmosphere feels like an evening in heaven: midseventies with open, starry skies. With full stomachs and hearts warmed by friends, family and now their first hosts, Aaron and Les retreat to their rooms with more than enough to relish on their first night of the tour.

Oh, California!

Aaron's alarm blurts into the air at 6:25 a.m. He stares blankly at the ceiling. He is quiet. The ride can wait. He thinks about how he and Les might feel at the end of the trip, in Delaware, or New Jersey, or New York. He imagines the stories they'll have then. He imagines new wisdom and experience.

His chest rises and slowly falls. He whispers a prayer to himself. "For an experience," he hears himself say. "Or for some kind of ambiguity and for chances to choose what kind of men we will be."

His pulls his thin glasses onto his face and reads his phone again: 6:30.

Les is seconds behind, closing his door just as Aaron is beginning down the stairs. They exchange looks of giddiness. It is day two—a day without festivities and good-byes. This feels like the first real day of their journey.

"Whoa," Les says, coming into the kitchen.

"Morning, guys!" Larry is smiling. He holds a half-emptied Gatorade bottle in his hand and is leaning against a cupboard.

"Good morning!" Aaron says, looking at both Janet and Larry.

"Think you're ready for today?" Janet asks, slicing an apple. There is a neat circle of at least three already-sliced bananas. "It's supposed to be a hot one," she says and looks at Larry.

"I think we'll be just fine," Les says respectfully. He moves over to shake Larry's hand.

"Okay, guys, come on. You need some energy," Janet says. Food begins to pile up in front of them. Grapes, yogurt, granola, toast. She motions Les over, waving off whatever conversation he is having with her husband.

"Now don't feel like you have to eat all of this," she says, setting out the last of the spread, a pot of hot oatmeal. "I just want to make sure you are plenty full before you set out."

"Thanks, Janet," says Les.

After breakfast, Larry joins them in the backyard dressed in jogging shoes, cargo shorts and a T-shirt that reads: "Redlands 100k." He casually reveals a map from his pocket, in a way that makes it seem to belong there. Opening it and pointing at their location, he explains the route he'll lead them out of Redlands on.

"It will spit us out on Highway 10," he says. "Then through a bunch of neighboring cities eastward. I'll be your tour car as long as you want me. To the end of Indio or to the end of the block, you just tell me when to get out of your hair," he says, folding up the map.

While Larry is speaking, Les pastes himself with a coat of sunscreen and says "mmhmm" often.

Aaron has been listening, though not carefully. He thinks instead about Larry and Janet's care and warmth. He looks back at the house and feels a strange guilt about how well they've been taken care of, a guilt derived from being brought up to believe he ought to work for everything he is given.

Janet hugs them as they step inside for the last time.

"Thank you for treating us like your own," Aaron says to Janet when they finish hugging. "Really."

"Oh, come on now, it's our pleasure. Now, did you get enough Gatorade?"

Larry rolls ahead in his four-door Saturn in the direction of the highway. For the first hour he remains around thirty feet ahead. Occasionally, he pulls up farther to warn them of oncoming traffic with the motioning of his arm. He glances back after every other block, giving them a thumbs up, and he falls back at times and then rolls by again to cheer them on: "Keep it steady, guys!" and "Looking good!" He is their tour guide, coach and biggest fan.

The road out of Redlands is hillier than expected. Ten minutes of riding and they are glistening with sweat, their nourishing meals now out to shine. They feel incredible. *Today is the day! Today is the day we just ride straight to New York!*

By 7:15 a.m. the sun begins to peek over the eastern hillside, creating a picturesque display of colorful, shimmering mist. The air is fresh and brisk, like mountain air.

At times, Larry pulls way ahead in the Saturn, and Aaron picks up his own pace, opening up his muscles and following quickly after. But, each time he does, he glances back to find Les gliding steadily in the distance, conserving his strength for deeper into the day's ride.

As they descend upon the Coachella Valley, riding parallel to Interstate 10 on two-lane roads that lead in and out of small towns, windmills the size of skyscrapers slice through the air with monstrous ease. Some clearly catch the direction of the air better than others, rotating their massive arms at high speeds.

The valley is a funnel, ushering wind east by southeast between the mountains of the San Bernardino National Forest and Mount San Jacinto State Park and Wilderness. They careen through the funnel and into the valley, tailwinds kicking them to speeds of thirty and thirty-five miles per hour.

Palm Springs is a retiree's haven, filled with Crown Victorias and golf carts, between the hours of five and ten in the morning, everywhere. From ten until sundown, no prudent soul is found outdoors, especially during the summer. When they arrive, Palm Springs is a sweltering ghost town. They stop outside a cafe and sit at a table in a shady corner, snacking on breakfast bars and peanut butter sandwiches, courtesy of Janet.

Larry sits with them. He sips lightly from another Gatorade bottle and asks questions about the ride, about how their legs have been feeling and about what kinds of things they saw. Les describes riding out from underneath an enormous fan and being shot into the valley like a bullet. He holds up an invisible gun and fires down the road, imaginary bullets slicing through dancing heat waves.

They have twenty-four miles before arriving in Indio where they plan to stay the night. It is a distance they are both content with moving slowly across. No sense in pushing their bodies through the desert during the hottest part of the day. They estimate that it may take three hours and tell this to Larry so he can know when they plan to stop again. Pedaling down long, black, treeless roads is casual and easy and, at times, monotonous enough to become entrancing. Aaron finds himself bobbing in and out of daydreams about what Colorado will look like, or who they'll meet in Kansas or how New Yorkers will react to their loaded-down bikes.

There is a light but hot breeze coming from the opposite direction they are riding, and occasionally Les rides up to Aaron and pretends to choke on it. He holds his hand to his throat and makes gasping sounds and then says, "Drink before you're thirsty." This was another recommendation he had read on a bike blog, part one of a slogan that finishes with "eat before you're hungry."

When they roll into Indio, Aaron's leg and neck muscles feel especially rubbery, and both his and Les's arms and legs are smeared with a mixture of dirt, sweat and sunscreen.

Larry rolls up from behind and says, "Hey, how about lunch, guys?"

"I am definitely ready," Aaron says.

"Me too," Les says quickly.

"Good, what sounds appetizing?"

They survey their east-Indio options, which seem scant at best, but settle on a cheap Mexican restaurant.

The air inside is hot and predictably humid; it smells as though a giant salsa-and-shredded-pork humidifier is running. At a small, sticky table, Larry tells stories about cycling and about driving out to Indio as a young dentist on occasion to work in a partnering office.

Then he offers thoughts on the church, mostly concerning how hard the job of a pastor must be. As he speaks his eyes show his wisdom, and his hands, which motion and accentuate his words, reveal his passion.

After lunch, Larry finds a nearby Super 8 motel and insists on paying for their room. Aaron wants to protest but doesn't. He watches Larry pull out his credit card and place it on the countertop.

The motel lobby is well kept and smells like fresh window and carpet cleaner. Outside the window, he can see that the motel has two stories, a stagnant swimming pool and palm trees everywhere. Pamphlets on the front wall advertise shopping locations and places to golf across Palm Springs. He finds a map of the Coachella Valley tucked behind a series of resort pamphlets and opens it. He reenacts the day's ride, starting in the northwest corner, where Interstate 10 comes into view from the Redlands area. His dirty finger slides quickly down the interstate and then slowly along the Palm Springs backroads, displaying to the audience of other pamphlets where they rode fast and where they rode slow.

After check-in they follow Larry out to his car. Their bikes are leaning against the motel wall, and Larry looks at them distantly. He laughs and smiles. "It's been a treat, gentlemen. A real treat. You bring life to old guys like me in letting me be a part of your tour."

They hug and then watch Larry get into his car again. As he drives away, his smile is still wide, and he waves goodbye one last time.

"Les," Aaron says. He is steadying his bike with his arms.

"Yeah?"

"Today," he says, stopping at the threshold of their room. "Today is Father's Day."

"Oh," Les says. "You're right. You're totally right, man!"

"Larry was our dad today. He was like our dad today."

They rise at 3:30 a.m., when nothing in the world barks, alarms or speaks. Beginning in Indio and heading farther into the unforgiving California desert requires strategy. They planned their route the night before. If they could leave by 4:00 a.m., completely packed and on the road, they would have two golden hours before the sun would creep over the horizon and begin baking the desert floor and valley.

Les gathers partially dried laundry clipped on coat hangers as Aaron rounds up water bottles, bike tools and pieces of fruit that are scattered across the motel carpet. They saddle their panniers, pulling straps and hooks snug. Next, they bungee their sleeping bags and mats down, and for Aaron, the tent, and Les, a small cooler that holds carrots, apples and yogurt from Janet. They speak with delirious efficiency.

"Hungry?"

"Yes."

"Dirty?"

"No."

"Ready?"

"No."

As they pull shirts, shorts and socks over their bodies, Aaron sits and stares at the loaded bikes leaning against the wall by the door. He thinks of all the people in the world who are asleep. *They are sane, and we are insane. For so many reasons, this is insane, Les.*

Les throws a banana across the room to Aaron and begins heating water for oatmeal in the microwave.

On the road, headlights are absent. *I could sit in the road and do anything right now and nothing would happen for hours. I could make a sandwich and read a book.* The only lights they see for at least two miles are their bike lights, which loudly blink across the road. Les leads to the highway where they will turn upon their first real grade of the trip, the Chiriaco Summit. The distance between Indio and the summit is thirty miles, with an elevation gain of about 1,400 feet. Thousands of tiny pieces of useless metal and debris line the Chiriaco shoulder.

With ease, and without sound or ample light, they make their way to the summit, which is a three-mile desert plateau. There is still darkness to spare. There are trucks parked at a rest stop, their engines humming. Within thirty minutes, the sun begins to inch into view from the east. They stop at a gas station to rest and watch the morning come to life again. Rays illuminate the endlessly deserted Southern California living room.

"Whew," Les sighs. "Nice to know we've dodged it so far."

"Yeah." Aaron bites into a granola bar. From the curb outside the gas station convenience store they can see the empty interstate. It descends east from the plateau and deep into a valley, disappearing into a blur of sand, hill and haze.

He sips from his water bottle and gazes as far out as he can.

Two cyclists arrive. They have come from the same direction, thirty miles up the hill, across the summit and down into the station. Their bikes are expensive and have no gear strapped to them. There is white powder in their empty water bottles. The riders quickly unclip, grasp their powder-filled bottles and click-clock into the store, trying without success to walk only on their heels. When they return, Les and Aaron watch the older one drink an entire bottle of powdered water. Like clockwork, he opens a new package of powder and dumps it into his empty bottle, refilling it with a bottle of drinking water he also bought.

dumps it into his empty bottle, refilling it with a bottle of drinking water he also bought.

The younger of the two cyclists notices them. "Hey, boys," he says. He stands beside his bike.

"Hello," they say and wave casually.

Several seconds pass. With the light there is a growing number of cars passing over the plateau and zooming down into the desert.

"Where you riding today?" Les asks when the younger one finishes his powdered water.

"Blythe," he says, his tone now more friendly. "We ride this every year. Our wives drop us off in Indio, and we meet up with them in Blythe to vacation." He takes another swig to catch whatever drops remain in his bottle. "How 'bout you guys?"

"Blythe tonight, and eventually New York," Aaron says.

"Oh, you're a long way off, boys," the older one breaks in. "But enjoy the ride. You will never forget it."

Les brings a tour card to the older rider and says, "We're keeping a blog. Feel free to check it out."

"Cheers," the older rider says, and then waves, as does the younger. In a moment, Aaron and Les can see them on the interstate again, gliding quickly into the desert.

Les snaps several pictures of the horizon, peering at the camera to see what he has captured, and then beyond it as if to confirm its quality. He secures the camera and looks at Aaron and says, "I wish I had a wife waiting for me in Blythe."

Aaron's dad said on the drive to the send-off ceremony that the desert would be hotter than he expected. And he was right. It seems incredible how hot it gets. By nine in the morning, when they are well into the desert, it is over one-hundred degrees.

They find a deserted cafe in a very nearly abandoned city called Desert Center, which truly does seem about as close to the center of the desert as it can be.

Aaron watches the bikes while Les carries their bottles inside. He bites into another granola bar and studies the empty land in every direction. Three semitrucks are parked nearby, and there is an old gas station with broken windows and boards on the doors. The café parking lot is not paved and has hundreds of dips and potholes. After four or five minutes the café door swings open. Les appears, looking irritated.

"They wanted seventy cents a cup!" He staggers.

"Did you pay it?"

"Well, yeah, but not after demanding why it was seventy damn cents per tiny, styrofoam cup. Turns out this place has to have their water flown in because they don't have water pipes!" He shrugs and hands Aaron his water bottles. "Man, this place... Just wow. Let's get the hell outta Dodge."

On the blazing and empty road, while pedaling up and down, they try to keep busy. They joke about how the massive semitruck tire shards, melted off from too much friction, look like snakes and walruses from a quarter-mile away. They plan defense tactics as they near the shards. They roll by the sleeping beasts with battle cries and the swinging of swords. They cheer as they roll on, unscathed and unharmed.

Forty miles after Desert Center they are both on their last bottle of water. Les pulls out a bunched up wristwatch from his pocket and brings it into view. "Almost eleven," he says. They are side by side, not exerting, just rolling, hoping that using little effort will retain the quickly evaporating water within their systems. Still, they cannot help but sip from their bottles every few minutes. The air is thick and heavy, like a blanket spread wide and just above the desert ground. Their seventy-cent-per-cup water feels weightier, more expensive on account of how much they need it. As it lessens with every drink, it is money and hope that seems to dissipate.

"Hey, man, I think we should pull over," Aaron says, shaking his bottle from side to side and watching droplets dance back and forth.

Les looks at the mountainscape to the south and holds his gaze there for several seconds. They have been riding along its unchanging peaks and valleys for several hours. "Let's stop at the next overpass," he says.

Every four or five miles the four-lane highway crosses over a forty-foot ditch. Beneath these ditches are rocks, tumbleweeds and cracked mud chips that crunch into dust underfoot. The ditches were made to channel rainwater underneath the highway and keep it from flooding, but only God knows how many decades it has been since this part of the earth has seen rain.

Shade is more than scarce, and ducking underneath the overpass is their only option. With nothing around them for dozens of miles, they are, in a way, desperate. Aaron wonders if he has ever been desperate for anything in his life.

They dismount on the overpass and peer over the ledge. They see tumbleweeds and a small, dried out channel that was likely created decades earlier to direct rainwater. Now, however, the channel looks more like the inside of an old, empty frying pan still above the fire, useless as can be. Aaron looks at Les and motions by nodding his head toward the shade beneath the overpass.

"What do you think, man?"

"It's about the best we've got."

"Seems our only option. What about water?"

He lowers it. He looks at Aaron and then sprints past him. He is running down the shoulder toward a car coming their direction. The car is a red blur, passing them quickly.

Aaron watches Les, who is still staring in the same direction.

"Aaron!" Les yells.

"What?"

"I've got no shame." He turns around and looks at Aaron. He starts walking back toward the bikes.

"What?"

"Hell, man, I've got no shame!" Les jogs now, and when he gets to his bike, he removes the other two empty water bottles and then does the same at Aaron's.

Aaron wipes a bead of sweat from his forehead and looks at Les. "What are you—"

"If God's gonna provide something, I don't plan on missing it." He takes three long steps from the dirt and onto the asphalt. Then, he holds every bottle he can manage into the air and waves them at other oncoming cars. He starts yelling at them. He grins at them; he laughs. He appears to be having the time of his life. "WATER! GIVE US WATER!" he yells. He motions at the bottles and dances like a sign twirler. He moonwalks. He does the Charleston. He swing dances with an invisible partner. Cars continue to pass, but at least now people are noticing. It is working. Kids have their foreheads flat against their windows. Their eyes are fixed on him, and their heads slowly crane as they pass.

After a few minutes Aaron takes a bag of carrots out of their insulated food bag and brings them to Les.

"This is going to work," Les says to a blue car passing. "People want to help people."

Aaron nods and hands him the bag.

Les takes a handful of carrots and stuffs them into his mouth. Then he yells, again: "WAA'RRR!" A piece of carrot leaps from his mouth.

Aaron ducks under a barbed-wire fence and makes his way under the shade of the overpass, finding it cooler than he expects. He considers camping here, their sleeping bags thrown out beneath the overpass as cars boom by overhead; it isn't such a bad idea.

Cars and semitrucks passing on the bridge above muffle Les's shouting, and Aaron thinks to pray. As he bites into another carrot, though, he finds this difficult. To ask God to provide a way out of a stupid situation that he knows is their own fault feels wrong. *We could have just been smarter. Why would God want to reward that?*

Still, he prays. Five minutes later he realizes that Les has stopped shouting. Aaron makes his way back to the road to take his first shift soliciting cars for water. He thinks about what he'll try. He could recycle the moonwalk; the sprinkler and the shopping cart might work.

he'll try. He could recycle the moonwalk; the sprinkler and the shopping cart might work.

There is something on the road now that wasn't before. Across the tailgate of a white pickup are the words "California Highway Patrol." Shit.

Les is standing next to the bikes, his arm coolly resting on his handlebars. When he hears Aaron approach, he looks over and smirks. "Told you."

"Told me what?" Aaron is trying to speak quietly. "This looks more like an air-conditioned ride to jail."

"Nah," Les says, waving him off.

Two cars pass, and a female officer in green shorts, black work boots and a khaki button-up exits the cab. A pair of black sunglasses cover her eyes.

"You guys alright?"

"Yep," Les says casually, both elbows now resting on his bike. His feet are crossed on the ground. "Just ran out of water a mile back. Didn't think it would disappear as fast as it did."

For a second she is quiet. "This is a bad place to run out of water," she says, nodding her head from Les to Aaron, and back to Les. "But, we actually have a lot of cyclists out here who run into the same problem. Hang on just a second." She turns and walks back to the truck.

"Think she's going to cite us?"

"No way, man."

When she returns she has six twelve-ounce water bottles in her hands. "You guys need any more than this?"

Aaron and Les exchange glances of shock and disbelief. Before they can finish thanking her, they are halfway through a bottle each.

She laughs. "Just come over to the truck and grab as many as you need."

A torn package that once held twenty-four water bottles sits on the passenger seat. Les reaches in for two more. Aaron notices the blast of cool, air-conditioned air hitting his sweaty arm.

"Wouldn't be so bad to go to jail in this thing," Les says, looking back and grinning.

The sun is unrelenting. The kind of intensity that buries itself in whatever skin is foolish enough to be uncovered. Every other mile the road rises and drops, bringing drivers and riders to a crest, revealing the next two miles of austere desert. In this part of the desert, miles seem to drag like time attached to an oil tanker.

They approach a large, green road sign that reads:

REST AREA 2 MILES

before continuing on to the border. This was decided at 3:30 in the morning within their cool, cozy motel room. Had it been any other climate, and at a different time of the year, they probably could have stuck to the plan.

They pedal slow, placing the rest area ahead as their next refuge.

Three cars are parked in a neat row in a lot big enough for at least thirty. Les points to two concrete picnic tables with a slatted, wood-framed awning above that is doing a poor job hiding the sun. This picnic area is one of two places to sit. The other is more shaded and occupied with people.

After steadying their bikes against the tables, they gather as much water from an old bathroom faucet as they can. Each drinks an entire bottle in one, long swallow and quickly returns to the faucet to refill. Then they drench old bandanas and drape them across their foreheads. Standing next to each other and looking into the old, scratched bathroom mirror, they laugh and pretend they are gangsters.

They create a bike tent with a tarp, a rope and their bikes spread five feet apart. Les explains that he read about bike tents on a tour cycling blog. The tarp swims gently in a breeze, and they comment on the gratifying feeling of creating shade in a shadeless environment. They eat more carrots, drink another bottle of water and lie out to rest on their sleeping mats. Before long, they are asleep.

At 4:30 p.m. the sun is beginning to make its descent, though it is still far from setting. Aaron wakes and doesn't know how long he and Les have been sleeping. His sleeping mat is slippery with sweat, and his eyes are blurry. He is dazed, and for several minutes he does not move but soaks within the humidity caught beneath the tarp above.

Les is still asleep, so Aaron shifts his weight and stares at the tarp. A bead of sweat drips from his brow and into his eyes. He gets out of the tent and feels the heat and the air. The sun beats down, but the dampness on his skin is cooled by the breeze.

He considers gathering more water from the old faucet in the bathroom again, but his muscles are sluggish and depleted. This exhaustion makes him feel pathetic. He takes out his journal and peers across the northern desert valley where there are no roads but only brown and tan hills and mounds of dirt.

> This is not the trip I envisioned. There is no romanticism out here in this godforsaken desert. There are no fascinating people. There's no endless thrill in exploring the places we've been so far. I'm just sitting here, wasting away. I'm a plum under the California sun.
> Bike touring trips are supposed to be different than this. People actually ride their bikes, regardless of the heat. They keep their heads up, and they see beauty. They see it every-

where. Even in the deserts.

I could just go home now. What do I have to lose? Some people still don't know I've gone anywhere. Other people will understand. I don't take risks anyway. I'm not a risk taker.

He eases from the ground and onto the concrete picnic table. It is scorching. The bike tent nearly topples when he instantly bounces up from the burning table. His travel towel makes a good momentary seat covering, and when he's upon it, he stares south toward the highway. The landscape is open, dry and predictable. He watches cars pass in lines of color and begins to remember how badly he needs this trip, not just to go somewhere, but to be kept somewhere beyond his normal place of comfort too—to be forced to be open to whatever happens. Discipline begets an aptitude for further discipline. There is a sense of resolve he feels when he considers what venturing into the unknown for a longer time than what is pleasant might do for him. He considers how being disciplined through this experience in the desert could make his and Les's future adventures across America all the more meaningful.

Minivans and sedans roll slowly into the parking lot, engines humming and radiator fans spinning. Kids pour from sliding doors. Most are barefoot and violently tiptoe across the sweltering pavement, gambling with each step, and quietly whimpering until finally reaching the haven of shade under the bathroom overhang.

Les soon stirs and wakes, looking equally dazed. "I thought the bike tent was supposed to keep the heat out," he groans. "I think we better eat and drink as much as we can."

Aaron nods. He gathers the empty water bottles, while Les begins making peanut butter sandwiches. Better rested now, Aaron is more aware of what the bathroom looks like. It is surprisingly cooler than he remembers. A foul odor looms in the air, but the cooler temperatures residing deep in the cinder-block walls easily trump the smell. Aaron decides he would choose cool and smelly over hot and fresh any day—especially today.

The faucet is calcifying at its base and head and is smeared with dirt and fingerprints. At a quarter turn, there is an explosion of water like a geyser. He pulls his bandana from his pocket and runs it under the faucet. He slaps it across his face and lets the cool water run down his nose and chin. Salt drips into his mouth, and he spits.

The water bottles are too tall to fit under the faucet, so he collects two-thirds of their capacity each. With two bottles under each arm, one in either hand and a bandana dripping down his neck, he walks back.

"We won't make it the last twenty miles if there aren't other places to get water."

"Yeah."

"So we better not."

"Yeah," Aaron says. "I figured."

"Better to suffer here than out there."

"Yeah."

"You okay?"

"I am. I guess I just had a different vision in mind for this adventure, you know?"

"Yeah."

"Like something romantic, the kind of thing you only see in movies and read in books. Just two guys on the road figuring things out, and having an adventure."

"I hear that."

"But here we are in the desert, out of water, energy and the will to keep pushing on."

"We're burning water just sitting here," Les says reflectively.

"Right."

"Right. Well, I have an idea, and it might—no, it will sound crazy at first. But see it as an extension of the adventure."

"Alright."

"So I'm reading On the Road."

"Ah..." Aaron rolls his eyes.

"Hear me out."

"No way, man. Hitchhiking? Isn't that cheating?"

"Cheating to whom? I don't need to ride a bike across the country." Les is smearing sunscreen on his cheeks; his eyes are fixed on Aaron.

"But we're on a bike trip, which means we have to ride our bikes."

"Why?"

"What do you mean why?"

"I mean, why do we have to ride our bikes across the country this summer?"

"Well," Aaron says, thinking. "I don't know."

"So let's just hitchhike. I am alright with it."

"Really?"

"Why not?" He stops smearing and reaches for his towel to wipe his hands, his eyes still fixed.

Aaron shrugs.

After a third trip to the bathroom to refill water bottles, they decide to move their gear right outside the cool stone walls. The eastern side is more shaded with fewer steps needed to refill the bottles. More importantly, there is more exposure to eastbound travelers.

They nod at construction workers, truckers, travelers—any and all who pass wanting simply to piss and keep moving. It is not hard to gather attention either. They are like kids trying to sell chocolate bars outside of a grocery store, except they look like two worn-out white guys in cycling shorts with wet bandanas across their faces. Their bags, shoes and food are strewn across the pavement to give credence to their story. Curious children ask why they are sitting on the ground, and they get good at replying loudly, so their parents can hear that they need a ride somewhere.

Mostly, Les takes the lead. He makes conversation with a man with a pickup truck, a woman with an empty van and an old man with a station wagon. But after an hour of wet bandanas, smiles and nods, and twenty explanations of their story later, still nothing.

It is close to 5:30. Worry drifts in with the easterly breeze. Maybe it was a bad idea. Who hitchhikes anymore, anyway? This isn't Kerouac. This is real life.

"Dude," Aaron says.

"It's looking bleak, I know."

"Every time they approach and just walk by I feel my belief in this sliding further and further away."

"It'll work." Les is far from giving up hope. By now, his wet bandana is over the extent of his face and he is prostrate on the cement in front of the women's restroom. He is too focused on his belief that a ride will present itself to notice that his choice of resting spot is a bit strange.

A few steps behind a dad and his son comes a man in khaki shorts and a T-shirt. He is clean-shaven and average height and looks about forty-five. His jogging sneakers squeak on the pavement, and his hands are lumps in his pockets. As he passes, he gives the same curious look everyone has given.

Aaron smiles back at the man and moves aside to let him enter the restroom.

Minutes later, the man exits and steps toward them. "Where you headed?" he says.

"Blythe, or the state line," Les says quickly, sitting up, "or anywhere in Arizona really. We aren't picky."

The man laughs, his hands stuffed into his pockets again. He looks out at the landscape. "You guys touring?"

"Sure are," Aaron says.

"How far?" He leans against the bathroom entrance.

"New York," Les says.

This sends the man into laughter again. "From where?"

"The beach. We're only three days in."

The man nods and takes his time. "I never did anything like that. Very remarkable." The man suddenly stands up straight and looks Aaron in the eyes. He steps forward, his expression blank. His right hand is moving slowly out of his pocket and extends outward.

Aaron sits back and sees the man's palm, worn and padded. It is outstretched now at eye level. It lingers there, motionless.

"Edgar," he says.

"Sorry, what?" Aaron says, surprised by the man's sudden introduction.

"I'm Edgar. Espinoza."

"Oh!" Aaron relaxes. "I'm Aaron. This... this is Les." Aaron shakes his hand.

Edgar smiles and then shakes Les's hand.

"Where again did you say you are going?"

"New York," Aaron says.

"I mean where tonight."

"Oh," Les laughs and interrupts. "To the border, or wherever."

Edgar looks at the cement and holds his chin in his left hand.

Aaron slowly peers at Les.

Edgar looks out at his van and says, "Well, hey, you guys want a ride?"

They try to contain their excitement but fail. They both laugh out loud, which brings a perplexed look to Edgar's face.

"Sure, we'd love it!" Les says, almost yelling.

Edgar motions toward his van, and they pull their gear into their arms, taking no time to secure panniers and sleeping bags to their racks.

Aaron guides his bike with one hand, buries his helmet under his free arm with a water bottle and clenches down on a bag of bread with his teeth.

Inside the van, four large scaffolds are stacked almost to the roof. Edgar pauses as if he didn't remember how they got there. He looks at their bags and bikes, and then he looks at them. "Guys, I'm not so sure."

Les has already begun disassembling his bike. He is hard at work, and without looking up he says, "Oh no, it's fine. We can do it."

Edgar shrugs and laughs. "Well, okay then. Hop on in when ready."

Aaron and Les work magic, stuffing mats, sleeping bags, bike wheels, frames, panniers, cans of food and water bottles in every nook they can find.

Aaron climbs in and sprawls across a piece of scaffolding in the back, and Les takes the front passenger seat.

Edgar has a box of Snickers and a bag of cherries. He calls them his traveling food, and throws the cherries back at Aaron. The cherries hit Aaron in the chest and fall into a crevice.

"Oops, sorry, brother," Edgar says, smiling and looking into the rearview mirror.

The first twenty miles east fly by without thought. Edgar carries most of the conversation, and within twenty minutes they are not only rolling through the border of a new state but are mowing through an ice chest full of food.

Edgar is a recent retiree of the Phoenix school system. He explains with much excitement that being a teacher in Arizona is not a bad job to have.

"Wood shop and a cross-country coach for just over twenty years, at which point I was given the option to retire with a decent plan for my wife and me."

"That's amazing," Les says.

"Can you believe that? They are paying me do whatever I want now, and I'm only fifty!" He beams. The old cargo van bounces over cracks and dips along.

"I've never even thought about retirement," Aaron says.

"Ah, you won't have to. It'll all be a big joke when you're my age." He looks over at Les and laughs again.

"Edgar, what was the most rewarding part about being a teacher?" Les asks. It is the first question either have asked him since the rest stop.

"Ah, man, great question." He holds his chin again with his left hand as his right hand steers. "You know, guys, I have to be honest with you. I believe in the work of a guy named Jesus." He looks at them, and something like gears seem to click into place. He goes on. "He is all about showing people that there is a way out, do ya know what I mean?"

They nod. A smile is sneaking out upon Aaron's face.

"Absolutely," Les says.

"I don't know where you guys come from when it comes to religious things, but for me it's an everyday kinda thing. You never know what might happen when you wake up and say to God, 'Who do I need to talk to today?'"

There is passion rising in his tone. He is just getting started. He talks about his shop classes and how after a few years of teaching he did not care as much about teaching woodworking as he did about telling kids about how God can change everything. "Visible miracles didn't happen everyday. But invisible ones were happening all the time. It's all about being open, you know?"

Les nods again.

"Give you an example, a student of mine in wood shop seemed down one day. So I asked him what was wrong or if he needed to talk, but he didn't feel like sharing. Well, later that evening as I got in my car I felt the need to pray for him. Thirty minutes later, as I'm walking through the door of my home, I get a phone call. Who do you think it was?"

They are quiet.

"The kid from shop, and he was weeping. So I asked what was wrong, and he said he had a loaded gun in his hand and was ready to pull the trigger on himself."

"Whoa," says Aaron.

"Seriously," says Les.

"Guys, at that moment I knew I had choice to make. I could tell the kid all of the reasons why suicide was wrong. Or," he says, "I could choose to tell the student a story about how love and hope are right, and good."

A few seconds pass. The van hums quietly over the open road.

"Guys, have you ever been given hope in something?"

Aaron thinks of growing up in church for as long as he can remember. It makes him want to conclude that he has received hope in something, but then again, he has never felt the way Edgar's student felt on that day—he's never been on the verge of suicide.

"I told him that this life was not all there is, and that a man came a long time ago and taught about a future place that included poor people, and sad people, and happy people and people at the ends of their ropes, and that this man literally died for people like him so that he wouldn't have to. I told him that this man was called Jesus, and that he loved him and me, and because of that, that I loved him too." Edgar pauses again before saying, "Guys, I could have been fired on the spot and probably thrown in prison if my student had pulled that trigger. But he didn't. Instead, he and I wept together, and he asked me to tell him more about Jesus." He looks back at Aaron, still sprawled across the scaffolding, and then at Les. "That was the most incredible day of my life."

"Wow," Aaron whispers.

"Hey, I'll bet you guys think I might be a little crazy or whatever, but I'm dead serious. And, hey, you never know who you're going to talk to, right? You're going to be meeting people far crazier than me. That's a guarantee!" He throws his head back and howls.

Aaron and Les laugh too. A kinship formed.

For the next hour Edgar tells more stories and slides in jokes with Mexican phrases and undertones that they, at their best, can only humor.

They are forty-five minutes beyond the California/Arizona state line. Aaron mentions this to Les, but Les doesn't seem to mind. He is now almost fully reclined in his chair, his damp bandana strewn across his eyes. Echoes of Les saying he didn't need to ride his bike across the country fill Aaron's head. Aaron looks into the desert from the van window. Deep down, he knows Les is right.

"So, where do you guys want to be dropped off, anyway?" Edgar asks, looking back.

Les pulls his bandana away from his eyes and looks at Edgar. "Edgar, you look like you might be content driving us all the way to New York if we asked you to."

Edgar laughs again.

"But really, how far is Wickenburg?"

"Oh, probably only another half an hour if I take this highway here." He points at a junction sign. "Wickenburg sort of forms the top of a triangle between where we currently are and where I need to end up in Phoenix.

"You could let us off anywhere," Aaron says. "You could have a straight shot down to Phoenix if you let us out now."

"No, no, that's alright. I've got the time. Hey, look, I'm a newly retired man! I'll probably have to find more hitchhikers if I'm gonna make the best use of my time."

They all laugh.

"Well, to Wickenburg then!" Les says.

"To Wickenburg!" Edgar cheers.

The sun is setting upon the slowly rising Arizonan desert as they pull into town. Their would-be host for the night is sort of a friend of a friend of a friend of Larry's, a karate sensei named Doug Glass.

Edgar pulls into a gas station around dusk and points out a couple of good places to eat. "If you're looking for something truly authentic around here," he says with his hand in the air. "Well, you might as well just go to Taco Bell... " He trails off into his own laughter.

As they finish unloading, Edgar asks if he could leave them with "a word."

Les quits packing and looks at Edgar and nods.

"Guys, again, you're going to meet a lot of people out there on the road, and if you don't remember me, well, hey, that's okay. But if you don't remember Jesus, well, someday you'll wish you had."

"Thanks, Edgar," Les says.

They all shake hands. Edgar waves, and in a moment he is down the road in the other direction toward Phoenix.

Part II.

ROCKIN' THE BED

In elementary school, when I started to sense what fitting in with the other boys in my class meant, I concluded that the first step to winning their acceptance was wearing the same clothes as them.

I'm a white guy. Not that this has anything to do with race, but when a lanky white boy tries to wear clothes to emulate his friends who appear to be in the Mexican Mafia—Adidas or simple Nikes, Dickies sagging below the ass and cinched tight around the upper thighs with a buckle bearing your initials and a baggy, black shirt that said something like "dog pound" or "rockin' the bed" with a hand drawing of two rottweilers standing together in the bed of a low-rider truck—then it not only looks out of place, but it also looks kind of sad.

One afternoon my mom announced that we were going to go clothes shopping. We didn't do this often, so I sensed this might be a good opportunity to dig up some gems that my classmates might think were cool. While most families in my area went to the mall or to Marshalls or Ross, mine went to the Goodwill.

I spent about an hour rifling through T-shirts on hangers that screeched on the racks like dry sticks scraping windshields. I found two that I loved, and when I showed my mom, I was looking less for her approval and more for her grace. They weren't the faded green or blue Gotcha or Stussy types of shirts I'd always liked buying before. No, these were emblems I hoped would make me an acceptable member among my predominately Mexican friends. They were, in fact, a black shirt that said something like "dog pound" and another with two Rottweilers standing together in the bed of a lowrider truck with the words "rockin' the bed."

The first day I wore it, a Monday, I remember the smell coming off the dog pound shirt, even after running it through the wash. It was the undeniable smell all thrift store items are marked by—tart and reminiscent of Clorox. Especially after wearing it while playing basketball at lunch, easily sweating right through it, I found myself feeling at home in the scent of Goodwill.

I started wearing each shirt twice a week, being careful to alternate, but it didn't take long for this to be spotted.

"Hey, man, look at Mickey," my friend Manuel said to another of our friends. (Mickey was the nickname they'd given me after I'd ambitiously raised my hand at the beginning of the year and asked my teacher if I could go by my middle name, Michael. Nobody that year, except for my teacher, called me Michael).

"Always wearing the dog shirts, man," the other said.

"Rockin' the bed," Manuel read aloud.

"Oh yeah, man, Mickey's all about rockin' the bed, homes," the other agreed.

They laughed, and I felt embarrassed, misunderstood. I was most definitely not about rocking any beds. My bed was just fine. It didn't need to be rocked. I did have dogs though (and this turned out to be what sealed the deal for me when I was deciding whether or not to buy the shirts. I liked imagining these were my dogs on my shirts).

As I walked ahead, I pretended not to notice. I kept along, looking out at the birds, the swing set, the slide, the trees, the grass, the lunch tables, the kids playing soccer, the gum on the ground. I went on looking at everything. But inside, I knew something was wrong with me. Something clicked. Not only did I not get their joke, but I was some kind of imposter. A phony.

ALL-FOUR-ONE

Most afternoons after school let out in sixth grade, Manuel and I and our friends Victor and Adam left Laurel Elementary School through an alley at the back of campus. We'd kick a ball across the field and pass it back and forth until we'd reach the hole in the chain-link fence. There was graffiti on the wall then, and we'd run our fingers along it as we'd pass like paying homage to the homies who'd gone before us. We'd flip open gates, pass the ball through apartment complexes and parking lots, under bushes and beneath cars, until we'd make it out onto the street that led us to the community center.

The Brea Community Center was where a lot of firsts in my life happened. It was where I had my first cigarette with my friend Francisco; it was where I'd succumbed to the pressures of my friends to make out with my girlfriend, Angie, in front of them on the lawn while they waited for their parents to pick them up, and where I waited until they all left so I could walk home; it was where I learned how to play foosball in the game room, and how to steal sodas with Adam from the vending machine near the bathroom.

It was also where I learned what it meant to be in a gang.

"All for one," Manuel said one afternoon. He put his hand in like he, Victor, Adam and I were going to huddle up.

"All of us," Manuel then said. "This is family, homies." Out of the four of us, Manuel definitely looked the most gangster. He also told us that his brother really was in a gang, and so we, especially me, were inclined to listen to everything he had to say about being a gangster. "All four of us," he paused. "We're all for each other. Got each other's backs. All four if one of us needs it. We're gonna be called All-FOUR-One."

It was pretty creative, I'll admit, and it's no surprise to me that Manuel went on to run a successful marketing business later in his life.

I looked at Adam and he shrugged. He just wanted to go skateboarding or steal more sodas from the vending machine. But he threw his hand in and nodded at me.

As all four of our hands met in the center, I felt my young life bubbling with so much meaning. It was the beginning of a new family, as Manuel had said, and to it, I mattered. My identity as one of them, I was sure, was secure.

WHITE ON WHITE

All my life, I've only been in one fist fight. I avoid fights of all types, be they with fists, words, friends, flying dishes. Maybe this is because I fear their outcome. What if I lose? Yes, I wonder this. But what if I win? What will I have broken so that I can come out on top?

Nobody likes a bully, and I've always tried to steer as clear of being a bully to anyone as humanly possible. I mean this to a fault, of course. The opposite of a bully is not the kid who gets picked on but the kid who, in trying to win the bully's respect, becomes a bully unto himself.

The best way to do this is to keep giving of yourself, even when it doesn't make sense: give out of your insecurity, the fact that you want to fit in; give whatever it takes if there's a chance you might be cooler. Be the clown, and people will love you.

Laurel Elementary had two classes of sixth graders. There was Mrs. Timothy's class, and there was Mrs. Branch's class. To us, with this separation in place, it clearly meant that lines had been drawn and that two distinct teams had been gathered. Every lunch hour many of us would spend our time competing in whichever sport was in season. Soccer and basketball were favorites, but football and dodgeball were common too. At the lunch tables someone would yell, "Timothy versus Branch," and then we knew it was on. From there, a good amount of trash talking would begin across the tables.

What was very clear in sixth grade, at least to me, was the concept of the rivalry. Winning something mattered more than learning, and it seemed this was why we were forced to go to school everyday. We went so that we could keep winning.

I was in Mrs. Branch's class. The guys in our class were scrappy and somewhat thrown together. We called it ragtag, and we were Francisco, the strongest, most all-around athletic kid in school who was of Mexican heritage but spoke only English; Victor, the recently immigrated Filipino kid who could best anyone at sprinting or basketball; Darrel, an African-American kid who wore basketball jerseys every day, and was kept around mostly for his height; Adam, the Mexican skater kid who never really cared about the rivalry, but whom we always convinced to be our fifth man; and me, the sole white kid who was tall and energetic, albeit rather clumsy.

Mrs. Timothy's class seemed more put together, as if they were the A class and we were the B. Everybody in this class, save for one white kid named James, was Mexican, and they loved the rivalry even more than we did.

It was spring, and we were playing dodgeball regularly. Francisco got the ball, wrapped his heavy left bicep around it, trotted up to the line and rocketed it into the stomach of Juan, Mrs. Timothy's star soccer player, who instantly went down. The game halted as Juan, through tears and muttered curses, gasped for breath and held his stomach.

"Pendejo," Big Arturo said as he looked from Juan over to our side and then began charging toward Francisco. But as if the line dividing our team's sides was some kind of sacred rule, Arturo stopped at it and swore in Spanish, which only Adam from our side understood. When he translated, it was decided by Francisco that this act was a threat and meant war. Real war, as only sixth grade boys growing up around gang culture knew, meant an all-out brawl after school in the alley. "Timothy versus Branch!" someone from our side yelled. We proceeded to make tough expressions at each other (which we called "mad dogging") until the bell rang shortly thereafter.

It was another hour and twenty minutes before school would let out. Mrs. Branch had instituted a reading hour after lunch, which we all utilized to draw up the plan of our after-school attack.

"Mickey, you start us out," Francisco said, volunteering me. "Just sock James in the face and then we got your back." I looked at my hands and wondered if they'd ever punched anything. This was for pride and for the rivalry, though. It was for the fight. And I was the one fit to start it. I nodded at Francisco.

When the bell rang, our class mad dogged those exiting from Mrs. Timothy's class. We held our shoulders back as we walked across the playground, then across the grass, until we got to the fence. There, we waited. We were saying things like "I got'chu," and "respect, bro," and "Branch versus Timothy—Timothy's goin' down."

I placed my backpack plenty out of the way and decided to dust the ground with my foot. I was nervous and didn't know what this would do other than possibly show I knew what a fighting ground should look like: that it should be clear of pebbles and debris. Nobody questioned it so I went on and made things really tidy.

Timothy's class lagged a while, and just when I started thinking they'd backed out, out they came, across the field and wearing matching white T-shirts that their button-ups had been covering previously.

I looked over at Francisco. He watched them walking toward us like a coach, his hands on his hips and his elbows pointed out. "Let's go!" he yelled, but Timothy's class kept right along at their pace.

We became two lines of five boys facing each other. After five minutes, when exactly zero punches had been thrown and all trash talk had evaporated, when it had become obvious to everyone except me that nobody was there to actually fight, I looked across at James.

"Hey, wanna get this started?" I said. It was more out of concern that we may all wind up forgetting about the rivalry than it was out of disdain for James or anyone from Mrs. Timothy's class. It was a suggestion. A sacrifice to keep the fire burning.

"Sure," he said.

That was when I realized I knew nothing about how to fight. As I saw his fists rise, I copied him; as I watched his feet move, I moved mine too. James looked like a boxer, as if his Dad trained him after school. His shoulders looked bigger with his arms up and ready.

I hesitated, remembering someone saying to never make the first punch. James, however, must not have heard that suggestion since he came right up to me and landed a jab right across my lower lip. I was stunned. But, now that he'd thrown first, I knew nothing else really mattered. I knew the fight between Timothy and Branch would commence around us, so I stepped back to look. But to my surprise, my classmates and our adversaries stood on watching, like they were waiting to see what would happen next.

"Fight-fight-fight," someone yelled. "Fight-fight, white-on-white," the voice went on.

We were, I then understood, a spectacle.

Oh, what the hell, I thought. I lunged at James with my right arm and missed his face by about two feet as he easily danced out of the way and followed with a right hook to my cheek. My face got hot and I felt myself get mad. But not at James. James and I were actually friends. I was mad at my side, my team.

I tackled James and he went down beneath me. That's when the cheering began. Fists grazed arms, heads, shoulders. James' ears got red and he bit me on the leg. This struck me as being really extreme. What else might he bite? I thought. I pushed him over again and wrestled him into a pin. I knew I'd have to keep the fight here; otherwise if we rose again I'd likely lose. I had his arms pulled back near his head but didn't know what to do next. I looked up at Francisco. He was laughing with Big Arturo.

"Damn, Mickey," Manuel yelled. "You gonna kiss him or something?"

I wanted to stand and tackle Manuel, to pin his face into the dirt.

"White-on-white, white-on-white," Manuel started to cheer. It was like a scene out of some rough-kid movie. Next, the principal or teacher would break it up, and we'd talk it through in the office, resulting in some punishment, and then a flash to a nighttime scene of some broken home situation.

But of course, that wasn't the case. This wasn't a movie. This was real life, where two kids who felt out of place and who longed for something to make them feel accepted among their peers ended up fighting each other like animals to get it. My weight on James, his face turning side to side, his body squirming—I felt really stupid for doing any of it.

"Hit him, Mickey, hit him!" someone cheered. But James didn't deserve that. I didn't want to hurt him. I never did.

To end it, though, I pretended to wait a second too long and then I popped him on the ear and stood. Two friends came over to me, but by now I saw that everyone was standing together, intermixed. The rivalry temporarily dissolved. Two guys from different classes passed a soccer ball back and forth. I saw Manuel look at Victor. "Yeah man," he said. "James kicked Mickey's ass."

I could give myself to a side, to the beginning of a fight as many times as I'd want, but now I knew I'd never receive their respect.

Only Passing Through

Wickenburg looks like a stop-through town for everything from fast-food, gas, a bed and breakfast and, for Aaron and Les, Karate Sensei Doug Glass's dojo to sleep in.

The day's events have felt heavy, as if multiple days were crammed into one: early rising, desert riding, running out of water, a run-in with California Highway Patrol, running out of water again, sleeping in a haze of warm air, trying to coerce dozens of disinterested people into letting them hitchhike and, finally, a van ride into Arizona. They are more than ready to find Doug's dojo, both feeling the day's exposure to heat and near dehydration pulling them toward sleep.

First they take Edgar's advice, however, and stop through Taco Bell. While balancing a bag of tacos on a handlebar, a burrito in one hand and his phone to his ear with the other hand, Les manages to call and check in with Doug.

Illuminated across a semi-vacant parking lot is Morning Star Karate Dojo's storefront sign. The six or seven other small businesses surrounding Morning Star have long since closed for the night, leaving karate students plenty of room to come and go with ease. A five-foot tall Japanese-style fountain surrounded by an array of roses stands directly in front of the dojo. They roll up to see a class in session and lean against a pillar to watch from a bench in front of the garden, stuffing their faces with tacos.

Twelve students gracefully carry through stretches and rotations in near perfect syncopation. A short man with glasses and a stout physique paces around them. He must be Sensei Glass. As he makes his rounds he studies each student intently. He rarely speaks but instead communicates direction by stepping alongside students and gently guiding their jabs and kicks with his hands.

After class, Doug pushes the door open and waves for them to enter. He seems to have little concern about two strange, young guys spending the night sprawled out across his dojo mats. "Well, welcome," he says reaching out to shake their hands. "The dojo is all yours. Just pull the door shut and locked behind you when you leave."

After Doug makes his way home, they ready for bed with reverence, like understanding his dojo to be sacred ground. As Aaron lays atop his sleeping bag he feels his body calmly taking him under; a full stomach and protection from the elements, his mind is now at ease and his heart once again full of hope for the journey.

Edgar's ride not only caught them up to schedule by the end of day three but also brought them more than forty miles into day four, making their next destination, Prescott, only a sixty-mile ride away. So, they sleep in. When they rise, they pack with ease, yawning as they push clothes and travel pillows into their bags. They pull the door shut and locked, just as Doug asked, fill up on fruit and snacks from a grocery store, push up the road to meet US Route 93 and turn at the fork at US 89, which they take going northeast. "To Prescott!" they cheer.

The dreary brown, deserted landscape of Arizona is mysteriously hilly—far more than the Californian desert. The amount of time they spend cranking up along switchbacks and inclines of day four's final seventeen miles through the Prescott National Forest takes the same amount of time to ride the first forty flatter miles.

"It's just like in life," Les says, rolling emphatically toward a summit. He sings together words about the hill climbs and descents of life. "Life has hillclimbs, life has descents..." he sings in his normal tenor range. Then, as if he is suddenly gospel infused, he switches to his best baritone, sounding something like Johnny Cash and sings: "Both come from the hands of the Loooord..."

The cactus and sagebrush of southern Arizona's desert yield to sudden groves of pine trees with quaint cabin-like homes planted unsystematically along the hillsides, giving warm reason for Prescott's welcome sign to declare this place "Everybody's Hometown."

Prescott is a serene town full of college-age people with short beards and laid-back demeanors, carrying pint glasses filled with IPAs in their hands and cigarettes between fingers. It is built on a hill that slopes down for three miles and eventually veers east into the desert of the Prescott Valley. There is a courthouse in the middle of town that is surrounded by elm and eucalyptus trees higher than the eye can see. The town has typical grocery stores and familiar fast-food eateries, but it boasts mom-and-pop cafes, musty jazz venues and plenty of fine drinking establishments.

Priority number one becomes finding a place to cook. A park with a picnic table is ideal. When they come to a park near the courthouse, Aaron wonders aloud if the area might be campable.

"Nah, overgrown bushes and brush are preferable for stealth camping," Les says, likely reciting something he read while preparing for the trip. "Not a ton of that around here."

Just then, they hear the voice of a man from behind. He is mumbling aloud as if he is carrying on a conversation with someone. "Prescott, a bike-friendly town. That's right. Friendly to our kind. That's right."

They turn around.

His baseball cap is smeared with grease and dirt, and he wears a red flannel overshirt and cargo shorts stuffed with wires. He is wearing enormous leather work boots. He doesn't exactly look to be homeless, but he could be.

"Are you local?" Les says.

"You bet I am," he says looking from Les to Aaron. "Been here a long time too," he grins. "I actually live just over that hill."

They peer in the direction he points, attempting to make out a hill, or a mountain, or something resembling one, but only find the rooftops of nearby buildings. Aaron slowly looks back at the man.

"My truck broke down in those hills on my way to New Mexico," he says. "And I never really got around to fixing it. I just sorta stayed here. That was about ten years ago." He laughs. His forearms recline upon his handlebars. He is in no rush to get anywhere. He points at their bags and asks where they're going.

"New York," Aaron says while looking at the wires in his pockets.

"No kidding! The whole way? That's excellent. You know, there's this guy you should really meet. He's just down here at a bar. Name is Ryan, and he is going for Virginia in a couple days. I'm sure he'd love to meet you."

"No thanks," Les says. "Actually, we're getting hungry and need to find a place to set up camp," he says. "But it's great to meet you, and—actually what's your name?"

"Well, they call me Harry. It's not my real name, but you probably couldn't pronounce my real one anyway."

Aaron looks quizzical

"American Indian," the man says to Aaron, shrugging. They all shake hands.

"Hey you guys should really hit up this party," Harry says. "Hell, you can probably just crash on the owner's living room floor. I know the guy and he's always having people over. He won't be there, but if you guys want to you should come."

"Yeah, we're going to eat some food and then think about it," Les says.

"Right on, right on," Harry says nodding and smiling. He fits his clunky boots upon his pedals and says, "Well, happy trails." He waves and rides down the road. When he has turned the corner, Aaron and Les sit down in the grass and let their laughter commence.

They find a picnic bench in the courthouse park and Aaron begins heating up water for pasta. Les pulls out a book and sits at the table with it. He only holds the book in his hands, though. There is a concert of sorts happening on the other side of the park with people seated on blankets and lawn chairs. Other people are standing up and dancing.

"You know what," Les says, bringing his gaze to the camp stove, which has been battling the task of heating water while also fighting a slight breeze. "I'm gonna go dance," he says, standing and slipping on his shoes. He jogs toward the stage without looking back.

Aaron takes out his journal and pen.

> *I'm really not one for dancing, especially not in cycling garb. But Les has always been a bit of a cavalier when it comes to social norms. This much of him, maybe more than anything else, I know to be true.*

He glances up in time to see Les take the hand of an elderly woman in a floral shirt and lead her to the floor. Aaron laughs and holds up an invisible glass in the direction of the dance floor, pretending a toast to Les from afar.

> *Four days ago we dipped our back tires in the Pacific Ocean. Only in dreams do people dip their bikes into the ocean, roll into Prescott, Arizona, make pasta in a park and dance with old women.*

After dinner they ask a local outside Safeway where most out-of-towners camp. He tells them campers never really get bothered in a park down past the shopping center. They thank the man and roll toward the park for about another half mile looking for ideal stealth camping spots. Darkness has come and they switch their headlamps on. Toward the end of the park is a bridge, and when there are no longer headlights on the road, they roll their bikes down an embankment and up onto an island in the middle of a spillway. They scour the area.

"Looks pretty good, right?" Aaron says.

"Yeah. I think so anyway. This is my first time stealthing," Les admits.

They find a row of brush and roll their bikes into the center. Next, they cover their reflectors with dirty clothes, and after setting up the tent they cover it with one of their two green tarps. They climb back up the embankment and peer back down into the spillway trying to find anything resembling bikes or a tent.

Les holds up his hand and Aaron high-fives it. Twenty minutes later, when they are inside the tent reading, a pair of headlights pan across the island.

"Shit man," Aaron says.

"Don't say anything. Just lie down."

"I know—"

The lights pass over them twice and then they hear a truck engine rev and roll away. Les lies on his back and places a hand across his forehead. "Whew," he says.

The next morning is warm. They pack their camp and roll their bikes back to the road.

"There was that Safeway back up the road, just before the park," Aaron says. "For today's food I mean."

"Good thinking," Les says.

While Les shops, Aaron updates the blog and writes in his journal about their first experience stealth camping.

> As the night progressed, we found a discreet spot to set up the tent. Just outside of the city park we covered and locked our bikes and drifted uncomfortably to bed. We wouldn't have changed a thing.
>
> Hardship after hardship of heat, hills, and now camping in illegal areas, but still nothing great enough to deter us from the road. Nothing to move in upon our adventure, shaking its head and saying no or telling us, "I told you so." Nothing to say we were too naïve, too young, too idealistic to think we could accomplish a bike trip from California to New York.

The heat rising from the late-morning road is palpable, though nothing compared to California. Along US 89 they crest a hill and pull off at a rest stop to make lunch and fill water from a nearby faucet. The air around them is weightless and gently presses through a thin line of pine trees like an invisible choir constantly singing, *wooooossshhh*. The temperature is soft to the skin and the cool water from the faucet at the rest stop coats their throats. Les is enamored with the greenery. He stands on the bench seat of a lunch table and holds his arms in the air. "They're beautiful. Gah! Look at this place. The trees, they're beautiful!"

After eating lunch Aaron watches a man exit slowly from a car that has just arrived. He peers up at them and pretends to look past toward the bathroom. He has a car full of children, and he is probably concerned about letting them escape in the midst of a man standing on a table wearing spandex with his arms in the air.

Aaron cuts into an apple with his knife. "Do you think God could have known we would see this?" He says, slicing.

Les has his arms across his chest and now he is lying across the bench. "Could God have known it?"

"Yeah, do you think God intended this for people like us? For travelers. Did he know that one day man would blast through mountains with dynamite and pave roads and set up parks at the top of the hills that he made. Did he know people would travel to the top of mountains just for the sake of enjoying the view?"

"Or to use the bathroom?" Les points at the troop of kids now waddling their way up the steps toward them.

"Or do you think he made this and we got the chance to come and find it?"

"What are you asking?"

"I guess I wonder if God planned for each of us individually to enjoy certain areas of his creation. Like did he know we would see this? Or did he just make it and simply knew that some people would come and find it and some wouldn't?"

"That depends on who you think God is," Les says plainly. "And how involved he is with the decisions people make."

Aaron places their peanut butter, jelly, fruit and loaf of bread back into the cooler on Les's bike. Just then the man with the children reveals a backpack, which appears to have something heavy inside it, from the trunk of the car. Looking up at them again, he calmly walks to the dumpster, lifts the lid, heaves the backpack in and lets it thud at the bottom. He walks back to his car, closes his door behind him and drives away again with the kids in the back.

"That was unusual," Les says sitting upward.

"What could that have been?"

"Anything, man. Books. Rocks. A—" Les pauses and looks at the ground. He peers out at the dumpster and whispers, "A severed head."

"A what?"

Les trots down toward the trash and Aaron follows close behind.

"What if," Les says quietly. "No, no, seriously—what if this was actually a severed head? What if we just witnessed this guy getting rid of someone's head in a dumpster on top of a hill in Arizona?"

"That would be insane," Aaron says.

"Get the camera ready. I am going to jump in."

Aaron shakes his head and starts recording, walking up to the trash can with the camera first pointed upon himself. He says: "Sometimes when you're on bike trips across Arizona, and you stop at certain rest stops, and you notice people tossing bags into the trash—oftentimes it's severed heads. And so that's what Les and I are trying to find out, or at least we know that one guy threw—" he starts laughing "—a backpack in this dumpster, and uhh, it was a severed head, and so that's what we're doing here—" He turns the camera on Les, his laughter having overcome him.

"I'm a little nervous about this," Les says, throwing a rock into the trash. "Because what if we go in there, we near the bag, we unzip it and it really has a severed head. I mean this guy drove up, got out of his car, tossed the backpack in. And then—" he looks down and then slowly back up. "And then he just drove away." Les starts climbing inside the dumpster, while Aaron holds the camera steady and props the lid open.

"How suspicious is this, man?"

"Here's the backpack," Les says, bringing it into the light. It is old, worn and opened at two pockets. "It's light."

"Light enough to be a severed head?"

Les peers inside and reaches in. "There is—a bag of garbage," which he lifts out with one finger and tosses aside. "And a piece of paper—"

Aaron is laughing from the other side of the camera.

"And a thirteen millimeter socket—how boring! How boring!" he yells. "Why is that not a severed head!" He throws the backpack on the ground and jumps out, kicking a rock into a nearby row of bushes.

When they arrive in Sedona the day's ride feels as though it should be complete. Their legs have weathered another day of heat and hills, and they wobble like rubber as they exit a grocery store. Their plan is to stay with a host in Flagstaff they found on Warm Showers, an internet hub for touring cyclists looking for homes or yards to stay in with other touring cyclists. Their host's names are Bobby and Annie Grey, and from Sedona, they are still around twenty miles away from the Greys' home.

"Dude, I would be content stopping now," Aaron says, collapsing onto a bench outside of the store.

"We could camp here," Les says. "Except we'd have to call off Bobby, and Flagstaff might be a cool place to stop."

They look out at the parking lot without saying anything and pass a can of corn back and forth, sharing a spoon to scoop out the kernels.

"I'm just going to call him," Les says breaking the silence. "Just to see what he says."

"I'm fine with that. Maybe he'll give us a ride."

"Maybe," Les says. "It's ringing."

Based on Les's tone, Aaron makes out that Bobby has called them weak because they asked for a ride, but then says something about just kidding with them. Les finishes the call and turns to Aaron. "He's coming here. Doesn't live very far away, but he did make fun of us for not wanting to climb the last hill."

"I got that part."

"Said he didn't blame us though, and after coming from Prescott he wouldn't have wanted to do it either."

"What do you think about that, man?" Aaron says.

"About getting rides? I'm fine with it."

"I don't want to do it often though. Seems cheapening to our experience."

Les thinks for a moment. "But remember, the trip isn't about the bike," he says. "It's about the adventure. We should see this whole thing as a long retreat that gets us from coast to coast. The bikes are just vehicles that will accomplish that end. I don't have any regrets about Bobby, or Edgar, or anyone else who wants to give us a ride."

Aaron looks at the parking lot and moves the spoon back and forth inside the empty can of corn. "Alright man, sounds good."

When Bobby arrives he helps them secure their bikes to the roof rack of his Jeep, and they start driving north toward Flagstaff. He doesn't speak much other than to comment on their stories. Soon, though, he brightens. "So," he says, "you guys want to take the scenic route or the main route?"

"Scenic," Aaron says without hesitation.

"Somehow I thought you would say that," he says, turning on his right-hand signal and directing the Jeep from the highway and onto a dirt road leading into the woods. Aaron can see a small grin on his face through the rearview mirror. "There's a back road that leads up to my house. It wasn't really planned that way. Started as a fire road and locals just started using it. Just is how it is." His headlights dance along rows of trees and down into gullies as he maneuvers through the woods. Bobby says he is a seasoned cyclist too, but that he hasn't been on any real tours. He says he hasn't been on a vacation in a long time.

Bobby's home is medium sized. The garage and basement are accessible from the road, while the main living areas can be entered above, from the hill the house is built into. "Annie really liked this place," he says as they come to his street. "She said it would be nice if we had a home built into a small hill. I told her that sounded expensive, but after a couple years we made it work." Bobby pulls up to his garage and gets out. He looks up at the canopy of trees and seems to take in the bits of open blue sky that he can see. Les and Aaron watch him and then look up at the sky too. Were it evening, there would be stars, and they would certainly be more bright here in the mountains than anywhere else they've been so far.

When Annie gets home she is welcoming and hospitable, but only slightly less somber than her husband. She shows them to bedrooms in the back of the house, saying that they used to belong to their sons who have moved out.

"We're going out for Mexican," Bobby calls down the hall. He is holding a travel magazine and his flannel shirt is tucked into his jeans. His glasses are round and precise. "That is, if you want to come to dinner with us. That'll be on us."

The road levels out as they reach the Flagstaff city limits. Bobby and Annie live just south of the city. Annie doesn't talk much, but she is present. She gasps when Les mentions they ran out of water in the desert and she smiles when he tells them about the ride from Edgar. Bobby smiles a little too, and when he asks questions they seem to roll out of his mouth evenly. He asks about camping, finding food, water and, as any serious cyclist would, about flat tires.

Aaron and Les each order a beer at the restaurant, joining Annie, who has a margarita. Bobby tells the waitress that water is fine for him. They are seated in the middle of a moderately crowded restaurant called Salsa Brava. Chips are brought to their table as they wait for their food.

"So what made you want to do the ride?" Bobby asks.

They each reflect, taking a moment between dipping chips into the salsa. Les sits back in his chair and says, "Adventure. The road. The mystery. All of it. We wanted to get out of California and see other parts of the country, and we figured what better way to do it than by bicycle, right?"

Bobby nods and looks up at the wall behind Les. "And you, Aaron?" he says, looking over.

"Same in a lot of ways," he says. "But also, I think it may be to gather up some answers that can only be found on the road. Maybe to answer questions that I haven't asked yet. In a way I wonder if that's how life is. You know? We see and experience a lot of confusing things that often don't resolve or make sense in our lives until later on."

Bobby nods again and dips a chip into the salsa. "What has led you to that thought?"

"Well, probably my beliefs. My faith."

Bobby's focus is firm.

"I'm not trying to say my beliefs produce any easy emotional outcomes, because for the most part I think they haven't. But there's this thought I keep having that the hard crap I've had to endure might be building me up for something later in my life."

Annie has an expression of concern, but she nods.

"For now, of course, stuff about life can just hurt, and there's no writing in the sky that offers a lot reason for it. There is hope though, I think. Plenty of reason to have hope for the future."

Bobby takes another chip and nods. The waitress appears with a tray of food and sets plates all around the table. She mentions that she's around if they need anything else. She smiles and turns away.

Bobby and Annie begin eating and Aaron and Les follow suit. Fajitas sizzle upon a griddle in front of Aaron for the next five or six minutes, and when wrapped in corn tortillas and smothered in sour cream and shredded cheese, they sink deep into his stomach and soothe his body. His hunger has been alive and groaning for hours.

Before leaving, when they get back into the car, Annie says she needs to use the restroom. She walks around the front of the car and reenters the restaurant. Bobby is quiet.

"Hey, Bobby," Les says.

"Yeah?"

"You live in a beautiful area."

"Thank you."

"I mean really. This place is incredible. And you're wife is so kind and generous. And you live near some of your kids too, right?"

"That I do."

Les is quiet for a moment. "Would you consider yourself a rich man?"

Bobby runs his hands along the steering wheel and looks out at the road. "Guys, I don't really know anymore. Too much has happened in my life, and plenty you have no idea about. I don't always feel so rich."

Annie returns. When she gets inside she says, "Ready?"

Bobby nods.

The next morning Aaron's legs are stiff. He doesn't want to rise, and 7 a.m. seems to have come too quickly. He does the math as he lays in bed and counts nine hours of sleep, which should be plenty, though it has only felt like two or three. He can hear Annie talking in the kitchen.

"Good morning," Annie says as Aaron comes into the kitchen. Les is there and has already finished a bowl of cereal, which feels funny to Aaron. Even though they're both ravenous, he realizes he feels bad about eating the Greys' food.

"Would you like some breakfast?" Annie says. "We've got plenty of bread for toast, and we've got a couple kinds of cereal. Les here has been a quite a fan of the cereal."

"Second bowl," he says, grinning.

Aaron rolls his eyes and sits down reluctantly. "Sure, I'd love some toast. But let me. I'll get it."

"Oh no, it's no bother," Annie says as she drops two pieces into the toaster.

Bobby comes in from the garage and says good morning. He smiles at Annie who doesn't move but smiles back. "Well, guys, what's the plan?"

"I guess we're going north for eighty-nine. Then we're staying the course through Tuba City before going northeast again toward Four Corners," Les says.

"You're not going to see much on that route," Bobby says. "Then again, you guys are thoughtful types. You might wind up thinking you're seeing too much," he grins.

"Why's that?" Aaron says.

"Well, up there is Navajo Nation, and believe me, there's not a lot. It's about twenty-seven thousand square miles of unusable reservation land from the outskirts of Flagstaff north to the Utah border and east to the New Mexico border. It bleeds over into those states from there, but it's not very appealing. It's no wonder why the government off-loaded that land on the Native Americans. It's pretty pathetic and sad."

"I had no idea we'd be traveling right through reservation territory," Aaron says.

"You guys will be fine, but just get water as often as possible, because there really ain't much out there. Here, when you're ready, why don't you guys throw your stuff in the car again and I'll drive you up to the saddle by Sunset Crater park. It's basically straight uphill out of here for the next ten miles. I might as well give you a leg up on the trip."

Bobby refastens their bikes above his Jeep. Aaron watches as his hands work slowly and with precision, as a carpenter's carefully shaping the corners of something he's building. When he is finished he says, "Well, are you ready to get back to it?" They nod, and after saying good-bye to Annie, they are at it again.

"To be realistic," Bobby says. "You have something like one hundred and sixty to one hundred and eighty miles to cover before you're out of Arizona."

"That is pretty sobering," Aaron says.

"Honestly, I'm really pretty excited for it," Les says. "I mean, come on, we get to ride through Indian Territory on this trip."

Bobby, with his sunglasses on and his full, white beard now more plainly visible in the sunlight, is smiling from his seat. As he pulls into a parking lot just off US 89 at the saddle, he shifts the car into park. "Hey guys, you know what, this has been really fun for Annie and me. I don't know that I expected to have as warm of an experience as we did, including our conversations, but just know we'll definitely be following along with you on the journey."

"Excellent," Les says. "Glad to hear it."

"Also, Les, to respond to your question from last night, I think I was just caught off guard a little bit. But your way of looking into my life is certainly one way of seeing things. I guess I just want you to know that I appreciated the perspective."

Bobby detaches their bikes from his roof and takes a picture with them before waving them off. As they pedal toward the crest, Aaron looks back and sees Bobby pull away in the other direction. "We may never see him again," he says.

"That's a possibility. But you never know. We very well might see him again, or we might not. We have no way to know."

"Yeah, kind of changes the way I want to approach meeting people. I want to be the kind of guy who asks the best questions, you know? I guess I want my interactions with people to be real."

"Great goal," Les says looking over.

"Still though, I think I'm going to remember the Greys for a long time. There was something there, you know what I mean?"

Les nods, as he does.

They begin to descend. Onward, Aaron thinks as he and Les roll quickly away from Flagstaff.

After a long lunch in Tuba City, where they wait for the sun to start setting to avoid riding in the heat, they continue along toward the town of Tonalea. The highway is poorly lit with flickering street lamps, and they seldom see cars or people anywhere.

Riding like cowboys across darkened Arizona plains, Aaron feels an uneasy tingle on his spine anytime he cranes his head back to see only black night behind them. When they arrive in Tonalea around 8 p.m., they realize together that the town they had imagined is actually just three dark buildings and a couple dirt roads shooting off in opposite directions.

Somehow, now that they've stopped, everything around them feels darker than before. Their shoes crunch gravel underfoot as they walk around each of Tonalea's three buildings to see if one is a market of some kind. None are, and all seem closed or abandoned, so they skip instead to looking for a place to stealth camp. Since there is no sign of life, there are no campgrounds, parks or large yards either. By the side of the road and down an embankment, however, there is a large tree with low-hanging branches. Aaron points it out.

"Yeah, looks fine," Les says quietly. They move carefully down the embankment, steadying their heavy bikes and trying not to slip. They say little while they set up. They work like machines; the only noises that can be heard are their sounds of production: zippers being pulled, sleeping bags being opened, the tent being filled.

While working with their headlamps on, they do not even think to consider how much the light they wear illuminates their presence. Without their lamps, of course, there is no way they could set anything up. Aaron is first to hear something on the road above approaching. "Shit," he whispers loudly. "Lights off!"

They fumble for their switches, but by the time they have them off the vehicle has stopped on the road. They simultaneously hit the ground and freeze, hearts pounding deep into the dirt and tall weeds, hoping the latter is dense enough to keep them covered.

There are voices. *Any number of things could happen.* Seconds slowly pass, but eventually the voices trail off and the vehicle shifts back into gear. It rolls forward, as if to get a better look down into the embankment, but after a few more seconds the engine roars and it drives off. Still, they do not move for at least another minute.

When Aaron looks up and can't find Les, he realizes this probably indicates that whoever had been in the vehicle couldn't see them either.

"Hey!" Aaron whispers.

"Yeah."

"What do you think it was?"

"Not sure, might have been state troopers."

"Voices weren't speaking English though."

"How do we know the police out here even know English?"

"That's an interesting thought, I would have thought—" Aaron is cut short by the sound of a vehicle coming back from the other direction. It does not stop.

"Come on," Les says, rising. "I think that was them passing from the other side. Let's just finish setting up and go straight to bed."

Aaron rises to a crawl from his spot, feeling the warm flattened weeds beneath his hands, and makes for the tent to finish what they started. This time they keep their lights off.

Arizona as a whole has felt like a spiritual place, both for good and for evil. Tonalea itself has this dark feeling. Accompanied by the fact that it's deserted makes it feel evil somehow. It is probably fine, and maybe I'm making things up because I'm creeped out, but I don't want anything more to do with it. Normally our nights are spent reflecting on the day while reading, laughing and eating. But not tonight. Tonight we're only here to sleep; tomorrow, we're only passing through.

I WANT YOU TO HAVE THIS

May 2007 — thirteen months until departure

A couple days after agreeing to ride bikes across America with Les—an idea that had only heightened in its tone of ridiculousness, and therefore still remained a secret I'd told exactly nobody in an attempt to try to save face—I met up with my friend Tyler for coffee.

When Tyler and I first met he looked as if he'd fallen out of a Hollister catalog and landed at the entrance to my church, running his fingers through his hair and glancing around in a daze at all of the normal-looking people. He was soft-spoken, affectionate, athletic and passionate about social causes. He didn't have a dislikable bone in his body. We basically had to pry the women away.

At this point, I'd known Tyler about two years. He carefully approached with a cup of coffee in either hand, one black and one pearl white. He set the black coffee in front of me and took a seat across the table. Coffeehouse noises filled the air.

"So how's it going?" I said.

"What?"

"How's it going?" I said again. It had been a few weeks since I'd seen Tyler and we were meeting to catch up. "I don't know," I continued. "How's work?"

"Oh," he said, sipping his drink and looking at the table and nodding. "It's good." After a five- or six-second lull Tyler said, "Hey, so, you like that stuff?" He pointed at my coffee. "Like, you really like it like that? Just black coffee?"

"Only way to drink coffee in my opinion," I said, smiling.

"I guess."

"You still get your usual—small, extra, extra vanilla latte?" I said.

"You know it," he said, slurping foam from the lid. "Only way to drink a latte in my opinion."

"Did you know a quarter of that cup was filled with vanilla powder before any liquid went inside? And powder here means sugar—a quarter cup of vanilla sugar."

"Why do you think I get it?"

I shrugged. We raised our cups, and I made a clink sound. I looked out at the street.

The day was hot and dry, and heat radiated in small gas-like waves in the distance from the pavement. It was a perfect time to be inside in the air-conditioning and looking out at the California sunshine.

"So, how are you?" He said. "You just got back from… from… Man, what's that place called?"

"San Luis Obispo," I said. "Up there they pronounce it 'slow,' spelled S-L-O. But yeah, it was okay."

Tyler nodded. He waited quietly, sipping from his cup.

"I won't lie," I continued. "It was hard at some points. Really hard."

"You needed to get away, man. But wait, why SLO?"

"Well, I was hanging out with Eric one night after work—you know Eric, from church? Well, he works with me at the café."

Tyler nodded.

"He said I looked terrible and said we should take a vacation. He said he had buddies up there and that it'd be a perfect getaway. I was pretty much up for anything to get my mind off the situation, so I agreed. Still though, it was really hard. It had only been a month since the breakup, so things were still raw and fresh."

Tyler nodded again, looking more empathetic. "Man, sorry to hear. You feeling any better now than before?"

I looked across at Tyler. I wished I could put words to my appreciation for him, for his kindness and genuine interest in my life. "Yeah, man," I said. "I really am." I sipped my coffee. "One thing I wasn't expecting to cheer me up was this bike ride we took. I got to ride this cool, vintage road bike that belonged to one of Eric's friends. Just around town and stuff. Nothing fancy."

"Cool. How was that?" he said.

"You know what, it was peaceful. I felt free. Yeah—like I felt released from my thoughts for a while."

"That's awesome," he said.

"But in the end, I think I was conflicted."

"Oh?"

"Yeah, I've always been skeptical of using something to dull my feelings. Using anything, I mean. Something about that idea feels unnatural, you know? Something tells me I'm supposed to sit in misery to learn from it, like wallowing in pain is the correct posture to have. But as much as I say that I know desensitize myself."

"Like with beer?"

I laughed. "Well, maybe. But I mean good things, too. Like music for example. Sometimes I just blast my music and scribble down my thoughts in my journal like I'm ravenous, like I'm mindless. It's never anything substantive when I get finished and reread it, but I use it to keep my mind busy and unfocused on everything else."

"Like it takes you somewhere else?"

"Yeah." I nodded.

"So wait," he said. "I don't understand. Why is that a bad thing?"

I stared at my coffee for a moment and looked for the words that had been creeping around in my mind over the month since the breakup. They'd often manifested themselves as phrases that told me to feel vengeful and hurt, to hide or to lash out however I could. I wanted to bring those feelings to light now, this being a chance to make them known. But no sooner did I start digging than they seemed to have crept away, almost like they were never really there.

"I'm starting to wonder too," I said quietly. "Well, anyway, I wound up doing something impulsive. I got on craigslist when I got home and found a bike." I pointed at the Shogun locked to a tree outside. "Being impulsive feels weird too, but I knew I had to go find something like the bike I'd ridden in SLO. Exercise is a good thing, right?"

"No," Tyler said emphatically, which confused me. "What I meant was that I don't always think it's bad to use good things to help us move past hurt. Know what I mean?"

I thought about it for a moment. I did think I knew what he meant, but I also believed pain was pain; hurt was meant to be felt and rolled around in for a while. The point of pain was to eventually know why it was that it happened. Right? Everything happens the way it does so that we will learn something. That was why bad things happened—we suffer so that we can grow closer to knowing ourselves, and God, and so that we can grow up to teach those who come after us. That was the purpose of pain to me, and it was a deep-set belief I'd either skimmed off the top of some youth pastor's sermon growing up, or simply a flawed philosophy I'd developed on my own to cope.

On the other hand, I was beginning to see how this belief didn't stand very well by itself. For one thing, I was tired of wallowing in hurt. Relief was definitely something that sitting in misery was not granting me. If there had been a lesson to be learned I thought I would have learned it already, but onward and upward the hurt continued to go, along with my slowly appearing coping mechanisms—my vulgar tongue, my excessive drinking and my habit of sulking in the dark of my bedroom alone. I knew I was doing these because I wanted to stop feeling and to be released from myself, my bitterness and my sadness. I wanted to escape to a place where my emotional life couldn't follow me.

Sitting across from Tyler, with whom I, for some reason, couldn't remember the creeping voice of negativity or anger I'd felt when I was alone, made me realize something about friends and the people who loved me. I was glimpsing the reality that I mattered a great deal to my friends.

"So the bike," I went on, changing tone. "Do you think that's a good thing?"

"Yeah," he said, looking at it. "It could be a really great thing. But I wonder if you might be open to something more."

Confused again, I looked at him.

"We've known each other two years, and you've been there for me a lot. You were there when I went on my first mission trip to India, you were there when I wanted to start my own business and you were there often to help me run it."

I nodded.

He went on. "I've known some people who have really benefitted from what I'm about to give you. They've literally gone in one person and have come out a completely new person. I don't want you to say no either. I want you to think about this, and how much this will mean to you ten years down the road. Okay? Who knows, maybe you'll even write a book about the experience."

I hesitated. I was tired of feeling sorry for myself, but I didn't want whatever he wanted to give me to be something that garnered me pity. Reluctantly I said, "Okay."

He reached into his bag and pulled out an envelope. He pushed it across the table. "I want you to have this," he said as I took it into my hand.

I stared at it. He'd written my name across the front. He'd sealed it. Without holding it to the light I already knew what it was. But I didn't know what it was for.

"What do you want me to do with this?"

"It's all I can afford right now. But you're my friend, and you need it more than I do. I want you to go to your school and get yourself signed up to see a therapist."

I was quiet, and for a moment I could hear every little sound around the coffee shop. "Therapy?" I said quietly.

He nodded. "I've already checked how much it will cost. It's cheaper since you're a student. This will get you the first six months."

I felt helpless, but to Tyler, I could see I mattered. Here he was lifting me from the ground, making me believe it was possible for me to stand again.

"Therapy," I repeated, turning the envelope over in my hands. It had never occurred to me to consider that option. "Okay," I said quietly. "When school starts up again, I'll jump in."

I got up and gave him a hug.

POINT BLANK

When I was twelve I asked my cousin, Cam, if he wanted to beat me up because I'd chosen to become a blader while he was a skater. Bladers did tricks and stunts with rollerblades, while skaters did tricks and stunts with skateboards.

Cam looked at the rollerblade boots on my feet and laughed. "Why would I do that? You're my cousin. Besides, I gave you those blades. I used to be a blader too."

Going into seventh grade I learned it was the choice of some people to become bladers, as I had. This usually meant wearing really baggy jeans made by a company called JNCO, and doing grabs and jumps off of things with your blades on. Mostly, however, people chose to become skaters. It was both a fashion trend and a sport. Skaters in the '90s wore baggy cargo pants, backwards hats and skate T-shirts.

Only skaters who weren't good, or who were at least unsure of themselves, spent time making fun of and heckling bladers, even if it seemed like everyone knew that being a blader was second class. You would know a skater was probably good if he didn't comment on bladers; you knew a skater was a real skater if all he wanted to do was go skate.

Eventually I saw that skateboarding looked more fun, and after I spent a week trying it with my cousins one summer, I decided to become a convert. I started bringing my board with me to school, church and friend's houses alike. Still, I feared the idea of meeting a pack of bladers and paying the price for committing apostasy. I don't know why I always feared choosing the wrong side, or displeasing others, or getting beat up. But I did.

My first respectable skateboard deck was a used Birdhouse deck with blue grip tape (the sandpapery top of a skateboard) from my cousin Cam. It was old and he didn't need it anymore, so he'd handed it right over to me, just like he'd done with his rollerblades. I got a pair of trucks (essentially the two axles beneath the board) for Christmas from my parents, and I traded Offspring's Smash CD for a set of Spitfire wheels with my friend Adam.

Cam was the older brother I'd always wanted. I wanted to be cool around him, and I wanted to skate wherever he skated, but mostly I just really wanted him to approve of the hard skating I did when I came over to his house. His younger brother, Kevin, was more at my level, and when Cam was out practicing, working out his latest tailslide-to-kickflip-out, or 360-flip, Kevin and I would practice our ollies off the curbs.

My uncle, their dad, was always a jokester. But he meant well. We'd always roll our eyes when he'd try to say something funny. I remember him coming home one day in his black Mercedes and seeing Kevin and me laid out on the warm summertime grass.

"What's this?" he said pointing at us and then out at Cam who was hard at work perfecting his tricks.

"Tired, Dad. It's hot," Kevin said.

"And what's this?" My uncle said, turning my old board over with his toe and letting it fall on its back like a carcass.

"That's Aaron's board, Dad," Kevin smirked. "It's a real piece."

Piece of shit, is what he meant. I wasn't offended, though. I knew how bad it looked. Since receiving it from Cam four months prior, I'd practiced on it daily and put at least a year's worth of chips and scuffs on it.

"Oh," my uncle said, suddenly sounding like he thought he might have said something hurtful.

Kevin and I kept lying there and my uncle went inside. We watched Cam practice his nose-grinds on the curb that he'd waxed up, and I studied with special concentration his heel-flips, a trick I never could get right. Soon, we saw my uncle get in his car again and we waved him off while Cam kept skating.

Thirty minutes later, my uncle's black Mercedes came around the corner again and pulled into the driveway. He got out and said, "Hey guys, look at this."

We looked over.

"Look at this board I found." In his hand he held a brand new, freshly grip-taped deck by a company called Point Blank. It was candy apple red.

"Whoa," I said, coming over. "You just found that?" My uncle finding the deck on the side of the road somewhere seemed possible to me as my cousins lived in a wealthy area. Maybe lots of people around there had an abundance of skateboard decks they didn't need.

"You didn't find that," Kevin said, disbelieving. "Who's it for?" he said, seeming to wonder if it might be for him. He stepped slightly in front of me.

"I did," my uncle said. "I did so find it. I found it for Aaron."

Kevin looked at me like he'd just lost a school election, to me. "For Aaron? Why?"

My uncle looked out toward the street. "Cam," he called.

"Yeah?" Cam said, slowing his board with his foot.

"Come over here and put Aaron's new board together."

"What?"

My uncle held up the Point Blank, its glossy underside meeting the sun for a sparkle. I looked at it distantly and didn't know what to do with my uncle's gesture. I looked down at my Birdhouse deck and saw many of its imperfections. It looked small and dirty. *Is this what people think of me?*

Cam came over and examined the deck. Even at fourteen he had the keen eye of an artist (he went on to become a professional videographer). He knew instantly, just by its curves and formation, that it'd be a deck with a lot of potential. "This board's got a lot of pop," he said.

Cam went to work and I watched. He was knelt down and choosing the right tools to take my old board apart and to fix up the best skateboard I'd ever owned.

When he was finished he stood on it and smiled. "Oh yeah," he said. "This is definitely a board with a lot of pop." He kicked back and ollied up two and a half feet into the air from a standing position. I'd never seen anyone ollie that high in real life. He handed me my new skateboard. "Enjoy it, dude," he said.

This is Why We Ride

The world is wide and open in places like northeastern Arizona. There is nothing but grass-land and shacks built upon hills with gravel roads. US Route 160, part of the old Navajo Trail, starts at US 89 in the south and snakes its way in and through Navajo Nation, into Tuba City and Kayenta, the only two towns they find that have much more than hillside shacks and a single convenience store. From there, it acts as the highway of the Four Corners Monument before zigzagging east through Durango, Colorado; Wichita, Kansas; and Springfield, Missouri; and then disintegrates around the Missouri/Kentucky state line.

At dawn, from the bottom of the embankment along the side of the road in Tonalea, they rise and pack in a hurry in an attempt to make sure nobody knows they've slept there. There are three small, absent-looking buildings in town, one of which is a bodega. They stop in hoping to find breakfast, only to come away with pieces of old bread and warm Gatorade. The man at the cash register looks confused when they ask for water and finally points out a decrepit faucet protruding from the side of the building. He motions them out, speaking no English, and only pointing emphatically at the faucet head.

The wind is torrential. To ride thirty miles takes three hours, which is about six or seven miles per hour slower than they are used to riding.

It is hot too, so hot that while they break beneath a tree along the shoulder of the highway, Les discovers he can drink from a peanut butter jar they'd bought. It rolls down the inside of the plastic container at less-than-appetizing speeds and pours into his mouth like pancake batter. Aaron takes a picture and then takes a swig. It is warm and coats his mouth and throat, and when he breathes in he feels heat.

The next fifteen miles into Kayenta are more of a descent, and with the surrounding hills, they are not as disturbed by the wind. They pick up speed and try to make up lost time. They arrive at a Burger King and lock up next to a pack of German motorcyclists who wave and say, "Yes, we are touring too," and, "Good luck," when they mention they're touring across the country. After each eating several one-dollar chicken sandwiches and some french fries, they roll across the street to a gas station market with seating and a sign in the window advertising free wi-fi.

"I wouldn't mind another ride from somebody right about now," Les says, laying his damp bandana across his eyes. Aaron is at the computer looking at Google Maps.

"Eh, yeah. I mean we've only gone fifty miles, but I'm feeling pretty done too."

"Feels like eighty. Or ninety."

"I'm trying to start coming around, man."

"About what?" Les peaks through his bandana.

"Taking rides from people, not riding the whole time, seeing this as a broader adventure and everything."

"Yeah?"

Aaron nods. "I even started drawing this sign." He holds up a sheet of paper from behind the computer that says:

MEXICAN HAT?

and below it:

...or the Colorado State line, we're not picky!

"Nice," Les says. "I approve!"

Outside, Aaron slides the sign under his bungee cable and faces his bike toward the gas pumps so customers can see it as they walk up. He stands by. Several people laugh and give a thumbs-up, but none offer to give them a ride, even when Les takes a shift and starts doing cartwheels. After twenty minutes he comes back inside and shrugs. "We might be riding."

Aaron looks out at his bike and sees the paper flapping in the warm breeze. "Okay," he says.

It is twenty-one miles from Kayenta to the Arizona/Utah state line. The wind has mostly died, and they wrap around hillsides and suddenly discover monstrous buttes looming along the horizon in the distance. At their base they are blood red and shimmering, and their peaks are orange like tangerines. Each mile brings them closer to and more in awe of the enormous natural formations.

"Have you ever seen one of these?" Aaron says.

Les shakes his head. "You?"

"No."

They don't speak for a long time, effortlessly pedaling down into Utah's Monument Valley.

"Dude," Les says when they stop at the Utah welcome sign at the edge of San Juan County.

"Yeah?"

"I am so glad nobody picked us up at that gas station. This is amazing." He raises his arms and yells, "This is why we ride!"

Aaron yells too, deep into the valley, holding his arms in the air. "I am so glad we're out of Arizona," he says after their echoes have faded.

"I was done with it a while ago. Never expected it to be so tough."

"Who knew there were real mountains in Arizona?"

"Or Navajo Nation, or the Greys, or Harry with the wires?"

They are quiet for a moment. They lean against the welcome sign and stare back at Arizona.

"I take for granted places like this. I tend to judge them by their negative qualities. But really, it's been an amazing ride, man," Aaron says.

"And this is only day seven," Les says, blinking.

"Yeah," Aaron says slowly. "Oh yeah! Man, we've done so much already."

Part III.

The Dutch, Delirium & Utah in a Day

They arrive at a tourist stop called Goulding's Lodge, two miles across the Utah state line. There are dozens of Europeans in minivans who are taking pictures of everything from the buttes, to the valley, to themselves and their rental minivans.

Other than the visitor center and a lodge (where most of the Europeans seem to be staying) there is little else. Back against a rock formation protruding three hundred feet into the sky, they find a vacant church and decide to camp behind it. The rocky earth has retained the day's warmth, and the temperature surrounding them is enough to keep them from having to set up the tent. They find level ground and roll out their mats and sleeping bags.

As the Utah sky turns from dusk to darkness, stars emerge in swarms. It is like one enormous salt shaker has spilled itself across the atmosphere in every direction. Some parts of the sky are almost entirely covered in white. There are no streetlights along the roads leading in and out of Goulding.

The next morning, shortly after they begin to ride, they see a mirage upon the horizon. Waves of heat and oil dance along the highway miles ahead. Within it, two forms are being closed in upon, and soon they realize that they aren't mirages at all. They are two men on upright commuter bicycles. They aren't wearing sunglasses or cycling shorts, and they don't have water bottles, as Aaron and Les do. Their unbuttoned floral shirts flow in the wind, and they laugh as Les and Aaron slowly roll by. Their hands and arms are doused with tanning oil, and their khaki shorts are wide with wind drag. The only snug items upon their bodies are sandals. The men are laughing to each other while they wave.

Aaron and Les kindly and slowly wave back and within five minutes the men are specks upon the horizon line behind them.

"Did you," Aaron says. "I mean, did you see—"

"Yeah. That was like that scene in the *Wizard of Oz* when Dorothy arrives in Munchkin Land."

"Except Munchkin land is in Utah, and the munchkins aren't short and speaking in funny tones, but are two tall, half-naked, half-floral-patterned men who only speak laughter."

"Something like that, yeah."

"But I mean, did that really just happen? Are we sleeping enough?"

"Yeah, it did. It totally happened. We just passed two laughing Europeans pedaling through the Utah desert on holiday."

An hour later, Aaron and Les are stretching and snacking in the parking lot of a convenience store just outside of the Mexican Hat, a rock formation with a stone that teeters upon another stone. The air is dry and empty. One car comes in for gas, fills up and leaves. The convenience store clerk is behind a copy of *Us Weekly*.

As they ready to leave, they hear voices coming from the south. Aaron drops a piece of granola bar into his mouth and looks back. The mirage has, apparently, manifested again, only now the European men are rolling down an embankment with their feet outward and off the pedals, and they're careening into the lot. Aaron looks at Les, who has his eyes closed and is holding his hand across his face to contain his laughter.

"We passed them ten miles ago," Aaron whispers.

"Maybe fifteen!" Les yells.

"Yeah, maybe fifteen! How the hell are they only ten minutes behind us?"

Les is laughing out loud now. The convenience store wall is holding him up. He is hysterical.

The men are not sweating. Instead, they are laughing, telling jokes and smiling.

"Where you headed?" Les says through his gaping mouth as they approach.

"Yes, we are from Holland," says the first man. His accent is heavy.

"We are on holiday from home," says the second.

"And you've come here. To Utah?" Aaron says, looking around.

The men laugh, their teeth showing brightly, like rows of etched pearl.

"Yes, we love coming to America every summer to ride our bicycles."

"Well, welcome back to America!" Les says.

The men walk along smiling and disappear into the store. When they return they each have a gallon of water in their hands.

"Yes, friends, every summer we drive the RV through Utah, Arizona, New Mexico. Sometimes, we stop and jus' ride."

"We love Amer-ee-cuh!" The second one says reaching out to shake Aaron's hand.

The first one takes Les's hand and pats his shoulder. "It is beautiful out here, yes?" he says.

"Sure is." Aaron says.

The men wave again, just like back on the road, mount their bicycles and pull away.

Aaron and Les wait a few minutes before pushing out behind them. After five or six miles, when it is apparent that the Dutch guys are nowhere to be found, Aaron rides up next to Les.

"Seriously, I need to know if any of that was real."

Les smiles again and pretends to think but can't hold a serious expression for long.

They watch the horizon closely ahead just in case the men might appear again. Minutes roll away with roadway and silence. Only the sound of metal chains cranking, cogs and grease flexing joints. Wind passes through their helmet holes.

"Hey," Aaron says. "Remember the time when the Dutch guys we met on the way through Mexican Hat weren't actually real?"

"Yeah," Les says. "And remember how just when we thought they were mirages they sped past us on their e-bikes, which they quickly converted, laughing and yelling, 'STUPEEED AMERICANS!'"

They pretend to dodge the stealthy and vanishing men and fill the next hour with imaginary scenarios where the Dutch men might show up, laughing and waving. Sipping tea and waving at them in Denver. Making sandwiches in a cornfield in Kansas. Riding their bikes up riverbeds in Illinois. Riding up and over the Appalachians in Virginia. Riding across the Atlantic back to Holland.

It has been at least three days since they've seen clouds in the sky. Out here, where the air is dry and the sun seems to have nothing to stand in the way of its beating down all the more fiercely upon the earth, they ride along, layering their necks and arms with sunscreen as often as they can.

But Monument Valley is full of surprises, one of which is a sudden northbound covering of clouds. Aaron pushes ahead and points at the sky. It has been a week since they've seen clouds.

"Clouds, man. Look!"

Les takes out the camera and pulls in a picture.

"You never know how much you miss it until it's not there."

Cars and vans of tourists are present but scarce. The valley grows wild with sage and weeds in some parts, and the hills make structures like walls. A car will pass every half an hour or so, and they wave. They realize that the more inland and away from big cities that they get, the fewer people there will be. They will have hours and days where they may be able to count on two hands the sets of eyes of people that they see. They know, as Monument Valley continues to roll, that this is America's great backyard, beautiful in its tranquility, and fathomless in its emptiness.

At lunch they seal and send postcards in a tiny and vacant market in a city called Bluff. It has gasoline service, candy, soda and a place to sit. The temperature begins to dip outside, and they watch a breeze pick up dirt and dust and spin it in a circle.

"Think we've got a hundred in us?" Les says scooping yogurt out of a thin plastic container

"Is that what we're up against?"

Les shrugs. "It's about a hundred and twenty to Cortez."

"We can go anywhere we want, and we can ride as far as we want."

"Once we pass the hundred-mile mark I'm sure we'll be able to keep pushing."

"I could use a rest day, though."

"Me too. I'd say the coast to Colorado warrants a rest day."

Aaron nods and carves out his own scoop of yogurt from the container. "Okay, Cortez and a rest day it is then. But today we push until we get there."

"Deal."

The sun is beginning to make its descent. They are making great time. Their legs, like warm and heavy pistons, have been cranking incessantly for a week. Food, water and a simple will to keep going provide their energy. After they cross the state line, they find US 160 again. They know they have gone out of their way to see Monument Valley, most likely adding forty or fifty miles to their trip. Their stories of buttes and open landscapes and funny Dutchmen, though, are likely to outlast their lives. So it has been well worth it.

Three miles before US Routes 160 and 491 meet, they run out of food and water. Signs for the city of Cortez say it is only eighteen miles away. At this point, eighteen miles seems so negligible that they pull off the road and into an abandoned lot to wait until they are ready to keep pushing again.

"Maybe we'll meet an angel out here," Les says.

Utah, Arizona, and California are to the south. They can see the sun beginning to set upon the land.

"An angel of what? Water and food?" Aaron says cynically.

Les looks at him and then down at the road. "Yes. That would be really nice, actually."

They lean against an old concrete structure, which may once have been a visitor center or an old gas station. It is hard to tell. The windows have been boarded and whited out entirely. They break twigs in their hands and hum songs that come to mind.

On the road a white truck rolls down a small hill toward them. As it passes they see its brake lights engage and the vehicle come to a stop before reversing and pulling up to them at the white structure.

A man, possibly in his forties, and a little girl get out.

"Saw you guys about two hours ago," he says.

Aaron looks at the time on his phone. This was likely around when they got back on the 160 from the Monument Valley back road, probably within ten minutes, give or take.

"Oh yeah, going back toward Utah?" Aaron says.

"No, going the same way as you. I thought you guys looked a little scarce."

"Can we give them some, Daddy?" The little girl says.

Aaron looks at Les.

"Well of course we can, sweetie. Jump on up there and open the cooler and start passing things out," he says. "You guys need some food, snacks, water, Gatorade? I've got plenty."

They approach the truck. The girl is in the truck bed and digging through one of two four-foot ice chests.

"We're part of an Indian reservation community. Actually from Arizona, not Utah," he says. "You guys are more than welcome to anything you want."

"Wow, thank you. I mean really, thank you." Les says. He starts to open up a plastic bag.

"What brings you up to Colorado?" Aaron says.

"Oh, to buy food and water. It's cheaper. Maybe you guys rode through the north. Maybe not. If you did then you know that there ain't nothing in those parts of the state. And if there is, it's more expensive than anyone can afford."

"So who is the food for then?" Les says.

"My family and for the families in my neighborhood," he says. "We all put money into a pot, and once a week she and I," he motions to the girl who has just pulled purple and blue Gatorades out of the ice chest triumphantly, "we drive up to Cortez and hit all the good marketplaces."

"So you stock up and share with everyone in your neighborhood," Aaron says. "That's really amazing."

"Thanks," the man says. "It's the little things, you know? Hey, you guys get all you'll need? Still got a while until you get into town I'd imagine."

They look at their plunder: blueberry muffins, beef jerky, gatorade, and full water bottles. They nod.

"We were kind of wondering how we were going to make it to Cortez," Les says. "So thanks for helping us out."

"My pleasure guys, and hers too," he says, smiling.

The little girl, who has been watching them eat, turns and tugs on her father's pants. "Come on, Daddy, it's time to go."

"Duty calls," he says and waves.

"Of course," Aaron says. "But thank you."

The man and the little girl get in and drive away. The sky is slightly darker now and their arms are holding their dinner. They can see the Cortez city lights in the distance.

"You know, you mentioned an angel, and I have to be honest," Aaron says. "I didn't believe God was going to send an angel, just like I didn't believe we were going to find water back on the interstate in California. But then we did, and now here we are with plenty of food to get us well into tomorrow morning."

Les nods.

"You've always been so hopeful, man," Aaron says. "I wish I could be that way sometimes."

"You can," Les says. "It's possible."

"You know what we forgot," Aaron says when they start riding again.

"What?"

"We never got the angel or his daughter's name."

They come up to US 491. From there they turn north and immediately find that there is no shoulder to ride on. Traffic moves about 50 miles an hour, and there are two lanes per direction and no median. They ride as tight and strict to the white line as they can, but they know they don't stand a chance of being seen by every car. The sun has set, and there are no streetlights on the road, only headlights of cars pulling up quickly behind them.

After a mile they find a turnout and pull alongside a metal barrier next to a call box.

"This is insane, man," Aaron yells. He is trying to compete with the roar of passing cars.

"This is the only way in, and we're going to get flattened," Les says. "I guess we need another angel."

Aaron pretends to laugh. *Why do you think we can just keep asking God to bail us out? That's not how it works, Les. God doesn't just give handouts.*

After a few moments catching their breath, they pull onto the road again. Les is leading, and with no shame he places his thumb out into the road. Aaron does the same. With every approaching set of headlights they stick their thumbs out. Dozens upon dozens pass, and some honk, indicating they're a nuisance. But they have little choice.

After fifteen minutes and two slow miles, a big blue pickup truck swings over after passing them and nearly cuts them off the road. A woman's hand comes out the window and motions them to come over. Les scoots up to her passenger-side window and peers in.

They are not at a turnout, and half of the woman's pickup is in the first lane. Her hazard lights are engaged.

After speaking for about ten seconds, Les removes his head from the window and peers back at Aaron, giving him a thumbs-up. They quickly lift their bikes into the back of the pickup and jump in.

Her name is Fabiola, and she speaks with a Mexican accent. She points out several monuments and shops along the road over the next fifteen miles, little of which they are able to understand.

"Why are you riding on this road?" she says.

"We just needed to get to Colorado," Les says. "Actually, we chose to go to Colorado tonight. This was the best way to get there, so here we are."

"So why you ride at night? So you think peoples like me was supposed to give you a ride," Fabiola says looking over and smiling.

Les laughs, "Well, no, but I don't know. Maybe."

"You should be more sure about it," she says. "Always be sure about where you are going. You never know."

They watch the town of Cortez come into view. It is not enormous, but it is the biggest place they've seen since Flagstaff.

Fabiola drops them off at a motel in town and waves before making a U-turn and pulling out of sight.

"I liked her," Les says.

Aaron nods.

The neon lights of the motel flicker before them.

"Well, what do you say to this one?" Les says.

"Looks fine to me," Aaron says. "As long as it has a bed and a shower."

"Mmm," Les says as he rolls his bike toward the motel entrance.

WHAC-A-MOLE

June 2007 — twelve months until departure

When people cope with loss they do all kinds of things. Some drink, some shoot up, some rage and party until their bodies finally go limp, blank and unconscious. Some people eat; others starve themselves. However they cope, everybody deals with pain, which, in my mind, makes us all the same in at least one very crucial way: we all feel the pangs of hardship. For many it is an ache that seems to originate within the rib cage, right at the crest of where our ribs come together—a physical manifestation of worry, panic, anger. And to deal with it, we make our minds and bodies escape reality in our own ways because we believe there could be nothing worse than feeling in the present.

In what felt like the course of a day, I lost my two best friends—to each other. Before they got together I couldn't have been more certain that one day they'd both be at my wedding, one in front of me wearing white, and the other the first man at my side. How bedrock the concept of certainty, and yet, how cruel to experience the depths of its layers.

One way I coped was by pouring sound into my body and attempting to exercise it to exhaustion. I would pull the Shogun from my garage, swivel my iPod as loud as it would go and crank up and down the hills of North Orange County. Music would ring through my ears, my headphones like an IV meant for audio-endorphins. As I would crank I would feel my muscles getting ready to pop, and still, I'd keep cranking until my body was so exhausted that it would become numb. This was where I'd go to find myself dull and detached from emotion, and that was all I needed—an escape. A coma, even if only temporary.

Coping through drinking came almost as easy as blaring music and exhaustive exercising did. Perhaps coping mechanisms beget more coping mechanisms. I'm willing to think so.

One afternoon after a ride, I parked the Shogun along the side of Jared's house, in front of his trash cans and next to his old, creaky air-conditioner block. It was humming, pulling in summer air and converting it into something cool before pushing it in through the living room vents.

As I situated my bike, the check Tyler gave me to pay for therapy came to mind, as it had many times after long rides like the one I'd just taken. The envelope still lay unopened upon my bedroom dresser. I felt guilty that I hadn't opened it the day he gave it to me and made a quick call to put it to use. At the very least, I could have been walking through the decision to enroll myself in counseling with my friends, or weighing pros and cons, or anything really, but I'd done nothing.

When I opened Jared's front door I was welcomed by cool air conditioning. I wiped a line of sweat from my forehead and exhaled. But, as I stood on the landing just inside the door, wanting a moment alone to cool down before joining Jared and the others in the kitchen, I was finding it difficult to relax. It seemed that no sooner had I stopped riding my bike that my heart and mind begin to take me over with familiar feelings and thoughts of loss and betrayal. The heaviness in my heart seemed to instigate a sour, anxious feeling in my stomach. My mind then turned to worry. Within a moment's time I was panicking, alone, standing inside the front door of Jared's house and looking around the room.

By what I thought to be some miracle, I remembered a quick prayer my pastor had taught me called a "Prayer of Intention." He'd explained that it was centered around the idea of being open to God in all things. I whispered it aloud a few times: *Lord, I am here; I present myself to you. Here I am.*

I knew this was not supposed to be like a magic saying that would fix me or grant good favor. But as I closed my eyes and prayed, I *really* wanted it to be. I attempted to envision letting the words of this prayer permeate my soul, hoping it would suddenly lead me to feel incredible peace and rest. I was trying really hard to feel a calm come over me; I manipulated the words, molding and forming them to fit my emptiness, hoping for them to make me feel better, but when I couldn't determine whether any anxiety had left my body, I gave up. I opened my eyes and just felt empty and lost. I tried to dig up whatever strength I could, took a deep breath and walked into the kitchen.

The evening kicked off with a glass of wine with Jared and Janet. Then when Chuck arrived, we all had a beer. Then Chuck insisted that we have another. The four of us told stories, and I remember laughing, a lot. I had another. We played music loudly from the living room stereo. Eventually, we found our way into Jared's bedroom and started making knock-off Tom Collinses with lemon soda, ice and a whole lot of gin. Jared was calling them Fake Tom Collinses, and I watched the glasses line up.

More laughter. More stories. More rounds of fake Tom Collinses.

Soon, it was only Jared and me. He was laying out a blanket on the top bunk of his bed while I, on my elbows and leaning against the wall, said, "Where were they, man—"

He looked at me. "They all went home."

"No, no. Not them," I sputtered. "THEM. You know who I'm talking about." I did the pointer finger and thumb-trigger-gun thing with my hand and cracked a loose laugh.

He stopped laying the blanket out and looked at me. He didn't say anything. I kept chuckling because I thought he should have been laughing at what I said, and because I was drunk. When drunk, no reasonable or worthwhile thought does anything more than pop into view and quickly vanish, like that Whac-A-Mole game. For me, too much alcohol makes all my great and terrible thoughts and emotions into a sloshy game of seeing which one I might whack open and spill all over the people I care about.

"Alright, man, go to bed. Up there," he said, helping me up.

"I love you, man. You're such a good—" I burped and tried to stand by myself and realized the ceiling was spinning. Before I could burp again I found myself lain out on my back on Jared's top bunk watching the ceiling turn around and around. Each rotation made me more annoyed, and then upset, and then uncomfortable, and soon I was wiping the cold sweat away from my forehead.

When I came to, I realized I'd missed the toilet entirely. I climbed back up the bunk ladder and told myself I'd clean up in the morning. Then I heard voices and the hall light was on. For a few seconds, I wondered where I was. What's happened to me? The ceiling fan above me was spinning now, which irritated me because the ceiling and everything around me was still spinning, but in the opposite direction.

The next morning Jared made eggs, which I promptly vomited in his side yard next to the air-conditioner block. My bike still rested upon it, quiet and still.

"Sorry about the bathroom," I said, coming back into the house.

He handed me a large glass of water. I didn't want anything to do with liquid ever again, but he insisted and I took it reluctantly.

"Don't worry about it, man. You got about half of it in." He lied. He motioned at the eggs again. I shook my head and put up my hand to indicate I would not be wishing to visit the side yard again.

I felt like a terrible friend. I knew Jared was a great ally to have, but I didn't know him well enough to have thrown up at his house twice.

He sat down across the table from me. "You know, I've been in your situation before," he said.

I looked at my shirt and my hands and back at him. "What do you mean?"

"I mean getting drunk and having to hope and pray I have good friends to take care of me."

"I'm sorry, man."

"Dude," he said, looking annoyed. "Stop that, now. No more apologizing."

"Sor—"

He shook his head and smiled. "I and everyone else know you're going through a lot. This is a time you're going to need to just receive it. Receive our care. Okay?"

I nodded.

"Also, overdoing anything always comes back with a harder bite. That's what I've learned, anyway." He smirked. "But if you're still going to do it, even if it's getting drunk, it's always best to do it among friends."

Like Les and Tyler, Jared was selfless and determined to see me on the mend, this much I could see. My arm over his shoulders, his body propping me up, I wasn't walking just yet, but now at least I was better able to stand.

DAD

June 2007 — twelve months until departure

Leaving Jared's house, I was hungover and didn't feel like riding home, so I left my bike against the air-conditioner block and started walking.

On either side of the abandoned railroad tracks running between Jared's neighborhood and mine were narrow trails that cut through tall weeds and overgrowth. I started down one of them and soon saw a man jogging toward me in the distance. Within a few seconds I knew quite well the way he stepped and how he swung his arms; I could imagine the expression on his face, intent upon the ground ten feet in front of him, thinking, planning. I knew because he was my dad.

I suddenly felt ashamed. I'd never had so much to drink that I'd been hungover, and I couldn't say whether my dad knew I drank at all. Each step we made toward each other brought a greater feeling of anxiety. If I were to grasp for the anxiety in an attempt to dissect and understand it, it would have evaporated, similar to how I had felt when talking with Tyler and trying to say aloud the phrases in my head that told me to feel vengeful and hurt, to hide or to lash out. Now they'd become quiet, internal whispers somewhere that said I'd become a man from a different side of the railroad tracks, that my ways were not the ways that I'd grown up with and that my Dad simply wouldn't understand.

It was his disapproval that I feared the most, even though he wasn't a very openly disapproving person. In general, my Dad was always a laid-back, thoughtful type. But somehow the belief that he'd shun or disown me if he ever learned anything he didn't like about me set itself deep into my psyche. At some point in my young life I learned to fear the perception my dad had of me.

I knew there was plenty that I chose to do or believe that he wouldn't have done, especially in my late high school and early college years. At my age he probably wouldn't have accepted a dare to jaywalk (or jayrun) across I-5 in San Clemente at nighttime; he wouldn't have persistently thrown himself down sets of stairs on his skateboard until he landed the trick he'd come to accomplish; he wouldn't have driven down a road at 115 miles per hour with music blaring and friends screaming just to stick his head out the sunroof and feel the wind attempt to tug his hair out of his scalp. He definitely wouldn't have gotten drunk, this much I knew for sure. Not that he was against alcohol, he just wasn't the drinking type.

Growing up, I thought I'd done a pretty decent job of hiding my somewhat brainless side from my dad, and that to him, I was a pretty decent kid. To perpetuate this, on the rare late evening that he'd arrive home from work and feel like talking, or on the weekends when he and I might play soccer in the front yard, I'd resist sharing anything personal about what I was thinking about or starting to believe in—even things about God or about girls that he would have agreed with. I did this to avoid my divergent thoughts or beliefs that might derail me from the family train and leave me feeling around for myself on a different side of the tracks.

But somehow, it had still happened.

As I continued forward, desperately trying to think of some excuse for my morning jaunt down the railroad tracks in the disheveled state that I was in, I saw him start to turn. His head still down around ten feet in front of him, still thinking and planning, he jogged around a row of weeds and back onto the trail in the opposite direction, back toward home.

By my estimation, he'd only missed me by about fifty feet.

SHIFTING GEARS

July 2007 — eleven months until departure

Setting: Sunny. Slight breeze. You're wearing a t-shirt with the sleeves cut away, basketball shorts and running shoes. The Shogun is leaning against the wall inside the garage. Here you are looking at it. It is 11:30 a.m.

Plan: Figure out these gears, Aaron.

Facts: You see that the headset has two levers. The one on the right clicks when you move it toward or away from yourself and changes how hard or how easy it is to crank your pedals. Pulling this lever toward you makes pedaling hard, but with time, sends you going faster. Pushing this lever away from you makes pedaling easy, but doesn't keep you going very fast.

Thought: You don't like going slow. Shifting away from you to use the slow gears seems to have little purpose.

Solution: Either ride on flats or downhill, or when going uphill, don't shift into slow gears, even if it means standing up on your pedals and making your quad muscles burn.

Plan: Figure out why you don't like going slow.

Facts: Bicycle gears determine how fast a bike is able to go. However, the bike cannot move without will and strength—the bike is lifeless; it is a machine. You can use your will and strength to ride the bike—you have life; you are not a machine. You have control over your gears. On a downhill or a straightaway, when you shift toward yourself, results come fast and at a rate you don't have time to think about. On an uphill, when you shift away from yourself, results… come… slow… and often they feel as if they may never come at all. When going slow you can hear yourself breathing and you can come to start thinking your thoughts in your head and you can come to start remembering the times when you didn't hurt like you do and you can feel heat in your chest as if it's burning a hole and trying to get out.

Thought: You understand how to make the bike go fast, and how to keep it from going slow. You have all the control.

Thought: Going slow prevents you from using the bike to cope. If anything, it gives you what you don't want: time to consider everything in your head and heart.

Thought: Going slow connects you, gives you the space to get back into your head, and since you don't like having this space, since space feels burdensome and makes you feel pain, going slow therefore takes away your control.

Solution: Keep chain in the second and third highest gears and avoid the fifth, sixth and seventh slower gears altogether.

Problem: You may run up against a long, steep hill that won't permit you to use your high gears. Then what?

Problem: Then what!

Problem: You're not always in control.

WE TOO ARE ROOTING FOR YOU

July 2007 — eleven months until departure

The weekend after getting drunk at Jared's, after I'd spent a week as far away from alcohol as I could, I took the Shogun out and rode it for four hours, my longest ride yet.

I started by taking it around the blocks by my parent's house, looping around and around, taking in the pervasive yet nostalgic scent of honeysuckle. I was a kid again.

From there I rode into the city. It felt great. I carved downhill corners on Lemon, rode by cars waiting at reds by the Brea promenade and sped into the Birch and Brea Boulevard intersection the very millisecond the traffic signal turned green.

In Anaheim I saw some friends I hadn't seen in years at a traffic signal, and when I waved they pointed at my bike and gave a thumbs up. I was proud and waved back, darting away as soon as the light turned green.

This was a great day. A day to feel like a champion. All the world in its rich and bright glory outside and around me just seemed to be waving me along, saying, *yes Aaron, we too are rooting for you. You're gonna be just fine.*

Some Kind of Pilgrims
(Colorado, Part One)

The shades are drawn but the sun is peeking through cracks at their sides. The room is quiet. The walls have brown paneling and their bikes lean naked against them, bags and luggage sprawled across the thinly carpeted floor.

"You want to go to church?" Les says from beneath his covering. He has his eyes closed.

"What day is it?" Aaron says from the other side of the room.

"Sunday."

"If we get up now we can probably still make a service somewhere. We'd need to use the internet to find one."

"True. What time is it?"

Aaron looks at the red numbered clock on his nightstand. "Nine-ten," he says. "We can still make a ten o'clock, we'll just have to hurry."

"I don't want to hurry," Les says.

"Me neither. I'd rather just stay in my bed and explore the city later."

The room is silent for a moment before Les sits up and peers at the wall. "Wait. We're in Colorado right now." Life has, apparently, returned to his body, and he leaps out of bed. Pulling a shirt on he throws open the door and looks outside. The door creaks shut behind him and stops at the threshold, leaving a sliver of light coming through the crack. When he returns, his eyes are wide. "We are in Colorado right now! Remember when we used to ride our bikes around Brea and Fullerton and down to the beach and talk about how the ride to Colorado would be tough, but that once we got there it would all be worth it?"

Aaron sits up in his bed.

"Well, we're here," Les says. "We've made it!"

Aaron raises a fist to the air in agreement and rubs his eyes awake with his other hand.

After using the lobby wi-fi, they find a church a mile away. The clerk at the motel seems indifferent to them checking out and then using the wi-fi. As they leave he waves.

The church is Baptist and the people are nice, quiet and mostly elderly. When Les and Aaron sit down, both wearing T-shirts and athletic pants with sandals peeking out, the congregation takes turns inspecting them. On Aaron's left are four open seats and a couple who appear to be about sixty-five. To the right, just on the other side of Les, is an aisle and then a cluster of elderly women with one younger family. As they glance at the congregants, none respond. In fact, the only person to do anything is an older lady directly in front of them who can't stop looking back and smiling.

"I think she likes you," Aaron whispers.

"Shut up."

After the service they meet a few groups of people, all of whom ask them who they are and why they found themselves at church this morning, to which they explain that they're from California and have ridden their bikes here, to Cortez, on their way to New York. Most, especially the elderly, are congratulatory. They say, "It's nice to know young and active people still think about church. Good for you."

Outside, they take their time unlocking their bikes as the parking lot empties of congregants in their cars one by one. This eighth day of the trip, they've decided, will be their first day off, so instead of planning out routes and pulling on spandex shorts, they ride into town in search of a cup of coffee and a place to do laundry.

They lock up in front of a gardening shop that has an outdoor patio and an indoor café. It is strange to see lawn flamingos and garden hoses hanging next to bags of coffee beans, but there are at least comfortable chairs.

Aaron finds a row of used books. Their titles are mostly foreign to him, but he recognizes the *Adventures of Huckleberry Finn, One Hundred Years of Solitude and Crime and Punishment.* He takes a sip of coffee and he pulls out one titled: The Way of a Pilgrim. The cover has an adorned Jesus figure wearing a king's crown and sashes and holding out an opened book in his left hand. Intrigued, especially by the title and the feeling that he and Les are some kind of pilgrims, he pulls it off the shelf and begins to read. Les sits across the room updating the blog and sending Warm Showers requests across their route through western Colorado. The room is warm, bright and tranquil. There is jazz in the background somewhere softly filling the air.

"I've never been so hungry in my life," Les says when he returns from the laundromat. "Have you eaten in the last couple hours?" He sits across from Aaron.

"No, but I want to. I'm super hungry too," Aaron says, setting down the book and lifting his coffee cup. "I'm getting the caffeine shakes."

Les nods and folds his arms. He looks around the café. "Only expensive stuff here. I'm gonna go look around down the street. I just feel like I could be eating all day. We're not even doing anything and I feel more hungry today than ever before."

"Could be that our bodies have adjusted to life on the road. They just expect to eat every hour. We're not giving them food so they are getting pissed at us."

Les nods and gets up. "Let you know if I find anything."

"Sounds good," Aaron says. "Oh, and Les."

"Yeah?"

"Want to ride up the street ten or fifteen miles? Get a little in without really breaking a sweat?"

Les thinks and then nods. "Yeah, might as well, I mean, ten or fifteen miles isn't going to hurt us. We might as well, and I'm feeling fine too, plus it'd be nice to get even closer to Telluride." He leaves and Aaron imagines the city of Telluride—the fresh, green forests, the dew in the morning and the awaiting Continental Divide. He stands, stretches and brings *The Way of a Pilgrim* to the counter to purchase it.

Thirteen miles north of Cortez is the tiny town of Dolores. One long strip of biker bars, maintenance shops, bakeries and mom-and-pop eateries runs through town, while quiet cottages lie up along the hillsides of the canyon.

They pull up to the Dolores Mountain Inn just before the sun sets. Their budget keeps them from going inside to get a room for the second night in a row. Instead they rest and Les occasionally gazes up at the sign along the top of the building.

Aaron is inspecting his tires. "Shall we just camp?"

"Side of the road?" Les turns his head and smiles. "Now we're talking!"

Aaron laughs. "Or maybe just at a campsite."

"Yeah," Les says exhaling. "Or that too."

"Camping along the road is just a ton of work," Aaron says. He wonders if Les thinks he is just making excuses.

Les shrugs. "I guess."

Two miles farther is an RV park that appears to be closed. They roll by the check-in booth and look inside. There is a light on, but nobody comes to the door when Les knocks. "Should we just go find a place to set up?" He says.

Aaron shrugs. As they begin to leave a man suddenly appears from around the corner. He is slow, and he is tall. He seems to get taller the closer he gets.

"Can I help you?" he says in a deep, raspy voice. He has a long, brown beard that covers his long face, and his eyes are deep and big. He tucks his hands in his pants pockets and they bulge outward as if they are holding stones.

"Just looking to camp," Les says. "Got any space?"

The man nods and pushes into the office. He picks up a clipboard and brings it out. "Forty bucks," he says. "Just tent camping, right?" He looks at their bikes.

Les nods reluctantly, likely thinking about how forty dollars on top of their stay at the motel last night is not helping their budget.

"Just sign here," the man says. He looks at Aaron and explains that it just means they're agreeing to the rules.

After Les signs and hands him two twenties, the man gets into a golf cart. "Follow me," he says. They ride along like dogs after their owner. The man leads into the woods and eventually points at an open spot. "Right along the river," he says plainly. "Be nice on a night like tonight." He nods and then accelerates away.

They unpack and lock their bikes to a picnic table, deciding to make chili over the camp stove.

Aaron rests on the table's bench and tosses small stones into the river while Les begins pouring cans of Hormel into their small pot.

"I'd love to own a coffee shop one day," Aaron says. "But screw the gardening supply thing. That's a little weird."

Les laughs and looks up at the sky. Their camp host in the golf cart is right about how nice the evening has turned out. The sky is a deep purple near the horizon line where the sun has set. To the east, the sky is opaque, and the half moon looms like it's drawn with heavy chalk. The stars around it cleanly salt the sky just as they'd done in Utah.

June 23, 2008

> *The river is fresh and inspiring. There is something pure and right about watching water move across the land. It feels unique, even though I've been around plenty of rivers before. On this trip, this is the first one we've been close enough to touch.*
>
> *Les and I are figuring this thing out every day. We have no idea what's next, but we're blazing our own kind of river across the country.*

Hours slip further into history, faster than ever before. It is the ninth day on the tour and they are learning how to manage their muscles, bones and bodies more efficiently.

"Drink before we're thirsty," Les says. He has been saying it about every thirty minutes, pulling out one of his plastic cycling bottles and slugging back a gulp.

"Eat before we're hungry," Aaron follows.

They cram granola bar wrappers into their jersey pockets. Eating while riding is just one of the rhythms they have developed. Others, including drinking water every twenty minutes and trading off leading every mile, have also fallen into place.

They follow Colorado State Highway 145 northeast along the river they had slept in front of the night before. The rippling sounds that had seemed loud in the night now seem docile and light. After two hours they feel incredible. Their day off has brought life and strength back to their muscles and they talk about riding for days on end. They could ride all the way home and back now, they say. This is adventure. This is vitality, survival. This is what conquering life feels like.

The road into Telluride is both more hilly and more serene than expected. Upward strokes, around and around, each revolution of their crank arms propelling them further into the Rockies. The effort needed to climb hills becomes an afterthought in the presence of the deep greens of pine and moss. They are far above the river now, and suddenly the road comes to a crest.

Les pulls off to the right and lets his bike slow naturally upon a gravel shoulder. There is a descent before them that seems to drop deep into the valley and off to the right around a bend, out of view. They do not speak. The clouds above move in herds. They watch them billow and take mighty forms. There are pockets of sunlight piercing through and placating a huddled army of trees like thousands of hungry soldiers awaiting long overdue rations. Les and Aaron hold their arms to the sky and wait for rays to break through the blanket and ignite their bodies.

Telluride is Bavarian, in a way, with large, dark brown craftsman homes lining quaint neighborhood blocks. There are gift stores and corner markets, butcher shops and inns. A school flying flags representing different countries, a small post office and a mail carrier on foot. Locals seem to drive extra slowly, as if implying that to hurry might interrupt something intrinsic, or that removing steadied eyes and palms from the road and car might scare serenity back into the forest.

"We need to eat," Les says, as they roll past a market. He is gazing back at it.

"And then a place to sleep."

"This market will do." They look for a place to lock their bikes.

From inside the market comes a waft of fresh produce and freshly baked artisanal bread.

The lighting is low and every display tag is handwritten. The floors are light brown and a man with dreadlocks, who is stocking apples, nods at them when they walk down the produce aisle. Check stands are to the left and all things organic to the right.

"What sounds good?" Les looks at Aaron. His face has a long day of riding across it.

"Anything, man. This orange..." he says picking up the melon-sized fruit. "Or that French roll. Cheese. Pancakes. Whatever."

"Nothing is cheap, not surprisingly," Les says.

"I'd share this bag of burritos with you," Aaron says, pointing at a freezer.

Les shrugs and slides them under his arm and walks toward the checkout.

Aaron watches the bikes outside as Les crams as many burritos as he can onto a thin paper plate and shoves them into a microwave near the butcher station.

"Did anyone look at you funny?" Aaron asks when Les comes outside balancing the paper plate with two hands.

"Me? No." There is steam rising from the plate. In minutes, they eat six burritos each. They lie against a concrete wall and hold their stomachs.

"So," Les says. "I was thinking—let's ask people if they know of a place to camp for free."

Aaron looks over and rolls his eyes. "That'd be really nice. I think I saw something when we came in. Some huge, white sign with the words 'free camping here' written on it I think. We should definitely go ask about that."

Les pretends to not hear him. His eyes are on the parking lot, his mind set upon a plan.

"Or," Aaron continues. "Maybe we can ask people if they know of some secret cave where cyclists sleep. Maybe they'll have burrito bags with them too?"

Les looks over and smirks. He holds the bag in the air and pretends to use it like a white flag. Eventually, he stands and begins greeting people:

"Hi, excuse me. Know of a campground, churchyard, backyard or public park around here?

"Hi, know of any well-hidden areas that we can camp in?

"Hi, we're from California and are going to New York. Can we pitch our tent in your backyard?"

But like the first couple hours at the desert rest stop bathroom before Arizona, nothing takes. People are kind, but none seem very knowledgeable about cheap lodging for transient cyclists.

As Les waves goodbye to an older man, a blonde, pony-tailed woman in her late thirties takes notice. Her face reveals conflict of some sort. Her eyes dart back and forth as if she is thinking.

"Excuse me, guys," she says, stepping close.

"Hi," Les responds cheerfully.

"I heard you mention you're traveling. What are you doing?"

"Well," he says. "We're from California and are riding to New York. We're just in town for the night and don't know where the best places to camp are."

The woman stares at them. Her right hand blocks the sun as she peers down at Aaron.

"Do you know of any places? A campground, public park, church...anything really," Aaron offers.

The woman shakes her head slowly and begins to walk away. But her face is lost in thought and visibly concerned. She stops, turns back.

"Hey, guys...".

Les stands, more at attention now than before, looking a little more concerned too.

"Well, why don't you just come to our house. My husband is the town doctor. We're just up this way." She points north.

"Uhh, okay!" Les says, smiling. He looks at Aaron who shrugs. It's as good as any other option. Possibly better.

They follow after her Subaru like dogs again, just as they had at the Dolores campground. Pavement flows like water beneath their bikes and heavy bodies. The woman soon pulls into her driveway.

There is a man inside who peers through the kitchen curtains. When he sees her stepping up the back porch, reaching to remove her rain boots, he also sees two young, mysterious men behind her. He lays down his dish towel and pulls the door open. Before he can speak, a tiny brunette girl is dashing toward the woman.

"Mommy!" the girl says, wrapping her arms around the woman like a baby chimp.

The woman is disarmed. She smiles and kisses the young girl and picks her up.

"Who are they?" the girl says. She is fixed on their cycling clothes and bags hanging at their sides.

"Hey, guys," the man breaks in. "Welcome!"

"Oh, this is my husband, James. Oh and—" She sets her wiggling daughter's feet back to the porch and holds out her hand. "—I'm Darlene!"

They all smile and exchange greetings.

"Hungry?" James says. "We've got plenty cooking so get situated and come meet us at the table."

The house is something out of a modern living magazine. Deep blue walls accompanied by a six-by-eight sheet of plated glass facing the street. Below, a basement with polished hardwood steps; above, a loft with two bedrooms and a bathroom. In the center of the living room is a fireplace with access from all sides.

Dinner is mostly steamed vegetables, lightly buttered and spiced. A tray of rolls meets the table next to a bowl of mashed potatoes. This second dinner is far healthier than their first.

The daughter, Solandra, or "Sol," as she says she likes to be called, watches them and giggles, especially when Aaron makes faces at her. She does not eat until her mother has cut her food for her.

James is distracted by two phone calls during dinner, but is otherwise happy to be entertaining. A contented look is on his face, but there is something else. As a weathered ship that has survived its share of storms, he seems now steadied along the shore, still operating, and still learning.

Darlene is less assured. She seems relatively distant and finicky, playing with her food as much as her daughter. Her blonde hair is now long and free, and she wears a simple blue sweatshirt.

The next morning Les and Aaron help with dishes after breakfast. Darlene takes Sol by the hand and announces that she will be right back.

"Day care," James smiles while clearing his plate into the trash. "Sol is our first of two," he says. "You wouldn't know this, but Darlene and I have been through a lot."

They stop cleaning and lean against the beige, marble countertop. The sun is in the sky outside. Soon they will be on the road again.

"It has hit her more than it has hit me," James continues, "which happens with mothers." James is quiet for a moment, staring at the table. "We lost our second."

"How long?" Les asks.

"Two years ago," he says. "So it's been some time now," he says looking at him. "The news of it sent her into a deep depression. It wrecked her, and our communication, in a lot of ways. I never thought it could happen to a couple like us, but it did. It happened to us." James nods slowly. "It's like a long, bad dream," he continues. "Count yourselves lucky you've never dealt with the loss of a kid." He holds his chin. "And hope you never do."

The house is quiet. Birds are somewhere in the backyard.

Les nods with James' words and Aaron looks at his mug of coffee.

"But that is life. And all we can do is decide how we're gonna live our lives around the shit that happens, you know?"

They both look at James and nod.

Darlene is walking up the sidewalk as they are pushing their bikes onto the street. When she sees them she holds her finger in the air, indicating that they need to wait, and rushes inside. When she returns, she has a camera. "Promise you won't forget us. Okay?" She looks younger now in the morning light. Easily ten years younger than her husband. She is smiling. She hugs them individually and insists on getting a picture with them.

She is happy and lively, something Aaron can sense is rare even in the short amount of time that they've known her. He is happy to see her smile, and something feels righted, if even only for a small amount of time.

In the summer the air is cool in Colorado. Its clouds are big and swell across the sky slowly. The ever-moving mountain air drifts through the fingers of pine thistle, channeled as southbound fronts from Wyoming.

They move on, eastbound.

Northwest from Telluride there is a long descent down Colorado State Highway 145. Then, they are northeast on Highway 62. They cradle the divide to their right, like ranchers, looking, waiting and watching always for where to split upward, through and over the mountain.

Three days. Today. Tomorrow, and the next. Then, we will brave the highest divide America has to offer. Stretching as far north as Canada and as far south as the scattered mounds of Arizona, the Rocky Mountains are a sleeping body with hips and a ribcage as its loftiest peaks.

In Montrose there is a Walmart and a McDonald's along South Townsend Avenue before Main Street calmly reveals a humble downtown where they pull off.

It has been five hours of rolling hills since Telluride. The day is still very young, and they know they can keep going. They are beginning to know their strength; their muscles are mending and appreciating the day off in Cortez peppered with forty-mile mountain rides from town to town. They are like engines, rhythmic in motion, up and down. Tiring less and less frequently. They know, but don't speak about it, that they can explode through Colorado. But they refrain.

Outside a nearby bike shop they eat granola bars before going inside. The owner is kind and personable. The way he speaks is as a man who yearns for the road and for his own kind of tour. He smiles and nods at their stories, but his calm and stilled body shows that he is committed to duties at home in Montrose.

Aaron buys a cycling cap that says COLOMBIA across the underside of the bill for no other reason than that he'd seen other riders wearing similar tiny caps. This feels right, like a rite of passage into the touring cyclist community. Motorcyclists wear vests with patches, and touring cyclists carry bulging panniers and wear tiny caps.

Les buys a new helmet. Aaron hadn't really noticed the old one Les had until now—the large, off-white helmet without its original plastic covering, now held together with glue and styrofoam and a salty black chin strap. Across commuting and training rides alike, he'd always had it though. Now, it had become more like a piece of dirty foam just getting dirtier. One could etch his name into it with his fingernails and flecks of white foam would lodge under his nails. Sweat and exposure to the sun had been dwindling its integrity for a long time.

"Alice told me I had to get a new one. She," he laughs, "She said if I didn't, then she wouldn't pick me up from the airport when we get home."

Aaron looks over inquisitively.

"I told her I'd just ride home alone then. And then she said I had just better get used to being alone then."

In the parking lot outside the bike shop Les holds up his old helmet, letting it dangle limply like a dead relic. He seems to reflect upon it. "You know," he says. "We should destroy this. Like, have an explosion ceremony to commemorate all of its work well done. Kept me alive this long, it's the least we can do."

Aaron slides the camera out of his back pocket and waits as Les pans across the semi-empty lot for something ignitable.

"On second thought. I'll just rip it apart with my hands and throw it on the ground. All on camera. I'll say something about the helmet and break it over my knee. I don't know. We'll see. Spontaneity."

Aaron starts rolling. Les walks into the frame and there are people in the distance with shopping carts going into a grocery store. The sky is grey, and blue. Les has his side to the camera and then throws his leg around and stares at the ground, dangling the crusty helmet from his fingers.

"This helmet would probably have saved my life if it needed to. It is only right and good that it would receive a departing smash upon the pavement like it was destined to. Nothing in it but air and the memory of how it held my head safe from becoming an obliterated melon upon the pavement."

A few seconds of silence.

"And now," says Les, with the helmet, raising it toward the sun. His arms are tight above his head, stretched like rubber bands. He yells: "Now we watch it fall!"

Hundreds of particles of white foam fill the frame. A black strap with months of white, salty lines is the only piece that remains intact.

Les is quiet. He looks at the camera. He steps forward and says: "This is what touring the US is all about."

So far, Colorado evenings have seen shelter. Tonight, it is a Warm Showers host in a small home two blocks away from Montrose Cycle. From their profile page, the Dalys are a young married couple who love adventure. That is about all they have to say.

Their street is quaint and narrow, and their home even more so. As soon as the tiny oak door opens, Les and Aaron are nearly bowled over by a black Labrador puppy named Sparky. He leaps into Aaron's lap.

The Dalys are instantly apologetic and embarrassed. They are Tim and Jenny, they say, and they all greet as Sparky now runs circles in the front yard. Tim calls him but waves his hand in defeat as the young dog sniffs and spins around seeking traces of other animals in his yard.

Jenny is average height with light, long brown hair, and Tim is tall with short blonde hair. He has a look of preoccupation as many newly married men seem to have, caught in the latest of matters to attend to. Jenny stands by her husband, beaming. She is more than ready to host in her brand new home.

As Aaron and Les are unpacking in the spare room, Tim enters. "Hey, guys."

"Hey what's up?" Les says, standing quickly.

"So we're headed to our church's mid-week group, and well," he says, studying the floor as if trying not to let something slip his memory. "It'll be like church, only at one of the elder's homes. You're more than welcome to join."

They look at each other and shrug. "We'd love to," Les says.

"Great, 'cause there's going to be a ton of food and I know how hungry you must be."

Jenny yells something about being able to throw something together if not. She has been listening from her kitchen. Tim says they'll all be leaving in half an hour.

Aaron and Tim trade sighs of laughter and annoyance as they dive after Sparky in the backyard before leaving. Tim says he hates having to tie his dog up in the garage. "It feels so restricting," he says.

When they do wrangle up the puppy, Tim reluctantly clips a rope to Sparky's collar and secures him in the garage.

On the road they all get more acquainted. Aaron and Tim talk about Sparky and share thoughts on learning how to be responsible for other living things. Tim might be recently married, but he's not naïve. He knows there are decisions far greater than he has now that will weigh on him later. Sparky is like a test, and if he and Jenny pass, then maybe they'll be ready for kids, he says. "Best to give the little things all I've got now so that I know a little better what it takes with the big things," he says.

As their four-door Subaru climbs a dark dirt road, making long, wide passes and switch-backing into the hills, the group shares bike touring stories. The Dalys, Jenny leading the way, tell of their honeymoon excursion.

"Excursion?" Les says.

"Yep," she says. "This guy talked me into doing a tour on our tandem for our honeymoon." Tim grins.

"Well, we were moving anyway. We're from Washington and we got married there, and we thought, or he thought"—she takes his arm in her hands—"that it would set our marriage off on the right foot to move somewhere new. But of course we couldn't do that without riding our bike there could we, Tim?"

"Just trying to be out of the ordinary. Unique and stuff. You know," he says.

"That's incredible," Aaron says.

"I got a job out here anyway," Time says, "and my parents drove our stuff out in a trailer. They actually set the house up for our arrival and we had sort of a post-honeymoon party. Also out of the ordinary."

Jenny's hands are still on his arm and she looks as though she is recalling everything silently. "I think if this were only his trip he would have kept riding," she says. "He used to lay in bed at night and say that the money we used for the house could have kept us touring for years."

"Four and some change," he says. "Can you imagine that? Touring for four more years?"

Aaron considers what four more years would be like on the road. He is inclined to tell the whole car he'd be up for something like it, feeling ambitious. But he doesn't say anything.

Tim and Jenny's church group don't comment on Aaron and Les's sunbaked faces and arms, but gather around and want to hear all about the trip. They ask: "Why forty days?" and "Why bikes?" and "What do your mothers think of all this?" Some of the older men and women press in with innocent inquisition, as if they were Les and Aaron's very own grandparents, aunts or uncles. They place their hands upon their shoulders and smile at their stories.

While strangers unto one another, there is a common kin-like warmth. Unlike church in

Cortez, there is a more relational bond present, something that feels familial. Aaron nudges Les and looks wide-eyed across the room emphatically, trying to indicate that this is the kind of communal hospitality to strangers that he likes. In a mere twenty minutes they have become like members of the family, as though they had been around from the beginning.

GIRLFRIENDS

I always wanted a girlfriend. When I was five I had a crush on a girl my mom babysat named Jenna. You better believe the first time Jenna was dropped off I told her everything there was to know about my house. I showed her the kitchen, the living room, the backyard. I showed her where the dishes went, where the bathroom was. I was pretty slick back then.

In fifth grade I had at least three revolving crushes going at the same time. Even when I had secured my first girlfriend, Becky, I still wondered what being the boyfriend of several other girls at school would be like. That was only a possibility, I think, because at the time I was somewhat of a novelty due to being one of the only non-hispanic boys. This meant I got a little more attention than others. This made me feel special, and eventually I came to crave this attention from girls. I wanted them to keep thinking I was unique and valuable.

In junior high I had two more girlfriends (at different times). The first one was Brianna, and the only reason we got together was because Victor was dating her best friend at the time and they'd said aloud in the presence of us both: "Wouldn't it be funny if you guys were, like, together?" I didn't think it would be that funny, but I was drawn to Brianna, sort of how put-together men can be drawn to women who are broken. She often wore a thoughtful expression, making her seem a lot older than any of her friends. Brianna was thirteen when we met, and by then she'd done more drugs, drank more alcohol and had more to say about which condoms were best than anyone I knew combined. But she never struck me as wild, just curious. She was so cool, and I loved it. I wanted her to think I was cool too, so when she told me over the phone one day that she thought it'd be cooler if I cussed more, I began cussing with her on the phone with great frequency. In the end, that was as wild as she and I ever got. It was a pretty harmless junior high relationship.

The other girlfriend, Tamara, bought me skater clothes. I could never afford them, but as a young skater kid, I desperately wanted them. She was always insisting on taking me to movies, having me over to her house to eat pizza and being sure to hold hands whenever we saw each other during breaks between class. I remember feeling like some sort of pet dog that wandered in and out of her sight. I was her tool and comfort. All I had to do was shake off the day's grime and hold her hand, and I was taken in. It was nice.

In high school I didn't date more than one girl. This might have been due to what I thought I was being taught at church. My youth leaders encouraged something they called having an "authentic faith," and from what I'd gathered, this probably including not dating until I had my faith under some type of control.

But I got tired of that. I gave in, as many of my friends seemed to be doing, and dated a girl from church, which was a way that I believed I could sidestep the subtle behest of my youth group leader's sermons. At least she's a Christian, I'd thought to myself. She was the sweetest girl, too, and also the quietest one I'd ever encountered. It was tough to get her to tell me anything about what she was thinking. This became a little annoying, and I didn't know anything about really dating another human being, so after three long, quiet months, I decided we had to break up. This was fine with me, too, as I was getting tired of feeling guilty for dating without keeping my faith under control.

I wouldn't date again for another three years.

TELL ME WHY YOU'RE HERE
(PART ONE)

August 2007 — ten months until departure

"So tell me why you're here," he said.

I didn't expect him to open up quite like that. I knew he'd be asking all kinds of questions. He was my new therapist, after all. But by the way he phrased his first inquiry I wondered if he'd taken the line right out of a movie. I had, however, thought about why I'd finally come. But it sounded so silly. It was cliché to come to therapy because of being heartbroken, right?

It had been nearly four months since the breakup, and I had learned to temporarily silence inner pangs by telling myself I had moved on, even if I hadn't. School had started, and I quickly buried myself in classes while putting in extra hours waiting tables so I could save money for the bike trip.

His name was Alex, and he was a therapist in training. When we greeted, he looked flustered. I stood and shook his hand and felt like one of us was about to be interviewed for a job. He looked around then, as if trying to find the best place to sit, and when he'd spotted the only other chair in the room he sat in it and put on an inquisitive smile.

"Well, I guess the reason I've come is kind of a long story," I started. "I've never been to counseling, or therapy, whichever it's supposed to be called."

"That's okay," he said. "That's quite okay. We can dive into things as slowly or as quickly as you want. The hour is yours."

"Thanks," I said, not sure what to say next or where to start. I'd hoped he'd tell me, actually. In preparation for this first session, I'd come up with what I'd believed to be several great opening lines and explanations for why I was there. In all honesty, I got it in my mind that this interaction should be epic, and I imagined myself as Matt Damon in *Good Will Hunting*. I wanted to seem unbothered, but deep, just like Damon did. Two of my best openers were:

"So I was dating this girl, and things went bad, so here I am."

And:

"We went on for almost three years. Marriage was, of course, on the horizon, and we had no idea that our lives were about to change."

But of course, I was sure it would go something more like this:

So, yeah, I dated this girl for two and a half years—and by the way, I don't want this to sound like some stupid reason for coming to therapy. I know you probably get a lot of people coming in because they've been heartbroken, which may be fine for them, and it could be that a listening ear is all they need, but in my case, I don't know, it all just seems really silly for me to be here to be honest. Who comes to therapy to talk about breaking up with their girlfriend anyway?

Fortunately, none of that happened.

"Well," Alex said calmly. "Like I said, the time is yours. We can talk about anything you want. How about you just tell me what's on your mind right now?"

I liked that better. It was more direct, giving me something to work with. The fire beneath the therapy pot was turned down, the rolling boil simmered. I started by telling him about Tyler and about how he wrote me a check to come to therapy. I told him that Tyler must have been crazy because he didn't have any money, but that he must have cared about me and could see how down I was. Then I told him that I didn't actually sign up for therapy for four months, and that even cashing Tyler's check to be able to pay for sessions was hard. I told him I didn't want to be in therapy.

Alex wrote notes on a pad of paper while I spoke.

I went on, telling him about riding my bike. I explained how I'd bought the Shogun from a thrift store in South County. "And South County," I reported, in case Alex wasn't from California, "tends to have nicer things, and hopefully this means my bike is halfway decent."

He smirked.

"I wanted to start riding a bike because I took this really great bike ride with my buddy Eric in San Luis Obispo. We must have ridden thirty miles that day. I remember not having much of a care about anything. I felt untouchable when I rode around that day."

Alex seemed to like hearing that because he glanced up and nodded and then kept writing.

I went on. "And, I guess that all led into a challenge to ride across America with my friend Les. His challenge, of course."

"Wait," Alex broke in. He sat up in his chair. "I'm sorry. Say that again."

"Which part—the riding across America part?" I'd expected this reaction. Anytime the ride across America came up in conversation people always sat up. I'd pretend to be humble, but deep down I was excited for people to know about it. I liked thinking that people would have reason to respect me.

"No, no," Alex raised a hand. "Tell me about what it's like to feel untouchable."

"Oh," I said. Now I sat up in my chair. By that point I hadn't really put intelligible thought to the emotions I'd felt while riding my bike. I just knew I felt free. "Well, have you ever been going through something hard and you just wanted to run away from it? I'm talking about just breaking off into the night at a sprint with no wallet, no keys, no shoes, no nothing. Just you and the road; or just you and the night communing, but without having to use words?"

Alex looked at the ceiling and thought for a second. A faint sliver of interest crept across his face. He held his chin and looked down. "You know, I don't think I've considered doing that. But I might be able to imagine it. It sounds like a scene from a movie with inspirational music playing in the background."

"Yeah!" I said, excited. I imagined myself riding the Shogun quickly down a dark road with the music of Broken Social Scene or Explosions in the Sky playing in the background.

"So you had this bike experience of being without a care, and you felt untouchable while riding," he reflected. "What was that like?"

"I guess, feeling strength in my body. Having the ability to move and control a machine, independent of outside forces, brought a lot of ease and satisfaction. Even now when I ride my bike, it's carving around corners at an angle that I'm sure I'll slide out from that really gets my adrenaline moving. Cranking up a hill and dripping sweat and feeling my quads burning—like, on fire, burning—or getting on a straightaway and feeling like I'm slicing through the wind as I stand up and push. It's a sensation I can't liken to anything I've ever experienced. It's freedom in a way. Riding has been a freeing gift."

"A gift," Alex repeated. "How so?"

"Well," I said, pausing to think and trying to define what Alex might take gift to mean. "Something given to someone else freely and without condition, perhaps." But that's not exactly what I'd meant. What I meant by "gift" was a little different.

Growing up in the American church made me aware of many ways that I was fortunate, or at least ways in which I'd received that others had not. I'd been to the slums of Calcutta three times; I'd gutted ghostly houses in New Orleans four months after Hurricane Katrina. Church also taught me that all good things came from God. These ideas sharing the same bed always came as a challenge to me, though. Or at least as a mystery. It was never a question of God's goodness, as in, "Why do bad things happen to good people?" Rather, it was a question of man's goodness, as in, "Why does good seem only to keep happening to those who need it least?"

I attempted to elaborate upon what I meant with Alex: "I think I've come to conclude at this point in my life that to receive something freely should mean some kind of responsibility to give that thing away to someone who needs it more. Sort of like blessings should always be changing hands. But, I've also found that this makes receiving anything gratefully pretty tough."

Now I took a second to look up at Alex, the counselor I'd just met, trying to gauge how my disjointed theologizing might have sounded. His demeanor wasn't affected, though. He still wrote notes and looked up at me when he was finished.

"So a gift," I continued. "I guess a gift is like getting something for free, something I don't deserve, but that comes into my possession anyway. Sure, I paid for the Shogun bike, and sure, Eric and I chose to ride those bikes for the first time in SLO, but I definitely still don't think I'm owed the amount of freedom I felt when I rode. I guess I've never thought I deserved to feel *this* good and *this* able to love the things that come into my life."

Electric Skies
(Colorado Part Two)

Fifteen miles into the day becomes the new standard for riding before stopping for a deep stretch and snack. It is just enough to get the body burning up breakfast and to get blood at a steady flow.

They stop at what appears to be an old campground but has now become a trading post, though nothing like those they saw along the roadsides in Navajo Nation in northern Arizona. The post has wood-framed house with vines lining the vertical beams, an outhouse-style bathroom and a small dirt parking lot with logs for curbs.

They stretch, chew granola and take in the greenery lying ahead in the distance. Aaron finds a patch of wildflowers by the road and abandons his stretching to pull a picture into his camera. They remind him of his grandmother and her garden. He thinks about printing the picture and what he'll write on the back. Something about Colorado's flowers being more beautiful than he'd have ever thought.

Aaron peers up at the mountains. An entire world lies beyond the Rockies; all he has ever known has happened along the western coast and its neighboring ranges. Will the grass bend the same, or the plains be green instead of brown? *Will the sky seem closer when camping under the great wide open?*

They take the day slow and easy. Monarch Pass, two days away, somewhere between Gunnison and Salida, is what they've been training for. It's been the single physical milestone they've talked about since the beginning.

That's it after this, Aaron thinks. From there we will roll down and out of the mountains of North America. We'll ride along the flats of Kansas, Missouri and Illinois. We'll cross lakes and snake through coal-mining country. We'll emerge upon the Eastern states and roll up to New York in style. All will come in its time, but not before the conquering of the divide; not before we battle the Rockies, our tallest foe, our slowest, steepest battle.

Gunnison is a college town. It has sleepy streets with antique shops that sell quirky collectibles. It has cafés, a Taco Bell, a school stadium in the distance. It has a Walmart, juiceries and mom-and-pop restaurants.

They lock up in front of the nearest café. It is a Thursday afternoon, and the café is a quarter full. They need the wi-fi to look up their Warm Showers host, Joe, to let him know they've arrived.

"His e-mail said just to drop by, but I just gave him a call." Les says.

"And?"

"Rang and rang. Nothing."

They lean into the large café chairs and don't say anything for a while. Aaron has a cappuccino on the table and his journal opened to an empty page. Les has his eyes closed and his face is relaxed, possibly asleep. Suddenly, he jolts awake. "Dude, let's just go. Let's just show up. We have the address. Maybe he was sleeping."

Aaron shrugs and sips his cappuccino.

Joe lives in a house with three roommates. There is a Jeep out front, and though they've been in Colorado several days, the green-and-white license plate still looks odd.

They knock.

Nothing.

Again.

Still nothing.

"So by 'drop by,' does he mean 'drop in'?" Les says.

"He knew we'd be here around this time. He couldn't have forgotten."

Aaron folds his arms and then faintly remembers sort of breaking into his neighbor's house as a kid. At twelve, it was entirely out of curiosity, a stunt his cousin had been pushing them to do for several days. Once inside, he'd felt a heightened sense of urgency and awareness of everything around them. The jar of pennies, the bag of half-eaten Wonder Bread, the paperwork, the uncapped pens and the VHS tapes stacked atop the piano would all be normal if they had been invited to come in, for these were the ordinary things that homes contained. But when pushing in without an invitation, it all felt strange and a little perverted. Like looking through a stranger's underwear drawer.

Les and Aaron have an e-mail granting some right of entrance, which they decide is easily open to interpretation. So, eventually, they use it and push in.

Just like being twelve again. Though they have Joe's consent, Aaron closes the blinds. There are dishes everywhere. The spice rack needs fixing and the yellow refrigerator looks as if it should be a little less yellow.

They sit on the living room couch and continue to glance around. Les suddenly stands and says he is going to shower.

"Shower?" Aaron says.

"We're here, and there it is," Les points. "So I'm gonna use it."

Aaron lies back.

When Les emerges, Aaron takes his turn. *A quick and essential wash.* When he finishes they've still only been inside twenty minutes.

"Want to go walk around?" Aaron says, knowing he won't feel comfortable until Joe has properly welcomed them inside.

"Sure." Les has his legs across the length of the couch and eyes upon a book from the coffee table.

Western State College of Colorado is vacant, probably because it is still summer. Some students ride by on bikes. A couple wave and they wave back.

They walk the length of the school grounds and come out at the main highway they rode in on. It looks different now. The sun has begun to set and buildings have taken up shadows. Along the southern sky are looming clouds that could be carrying six thousand pounds of water. But they drift by in their patches, serene, peaceful.

They stand and watch the sky for a while.

"This would be a perfect moment to say something profound," Aaron says.

Les looks over and blinks and then looks back. "If I've seen skies as electric as these then I haven't been paying attention. I've made a busy life the color of my sky."

"Whoa."

"Pretty good right?"

They laugh.

"Yes. Electric skies. I love that," Aaron says.

Just then, the sun bursts through the clouds and casts a stream of orange and dark red upon the southern sky above the foothills. There is a fire now, and it is unraveling, changing, growing here, and tempering there. It is all above, and now purple takes the background. Red, orange and white clouds are the paint upon a majestic purple canvas.

Aaron has been holding a section of chain link fence and it is making indentations across his palms. He steps back and peers out across the schoolyard quad.

"The students here get this every day. Football and track stars, they gotta attribute at least a part of their victories to these electric sunsets. Have you ever seen something like this?"

Les shakes his head. "And to think we could have missed it if we didn't walk over here, if we didn't feel so creepy about being at Joe's while Joe was out doing whatever he does."

Joe is tall, stalky, but not heavy, and wears a Michigan State T-shirt. "There they are," he says.

Aaron waves. "Joe?"

They approach and Joe waits for them to step up the porch before greeting.

"I see you found your way in."

It is silent for a few seconds. "Oh, yeah, we did," Aaron says.

"Good, very good. I'm glad. Must have pulled up right after you left again."

"Wasn't a bother. Dropped stuff off and took a walk," says Les.

"Beautiful sunset, right? Spectacular, I'd even say," Joe says. "Well, hungry?" he says, walking toward the kitchen. "I don't got much, but there are tater tots and hamburgers cooking. Want some?"

Grease, potatoes and meat are sure to fill the incessant hunger void of the touring stomach within. They both nod.

Inside, one of Joe's roommates is reading a map. Joe calls him Chad, and he rises to meet them. He is skinny, blonde and about six-four, towering above them. Except for his height, it is uncanny how much he looks like a younger version of Tim from Montrose. He is wearing a cross-country running shirt, and Aaron vaguely remembers the school's name from when he kept time stats on runners and teams in the early 2000s. Colorado always produced the best runners.

Chad is talkative. They quickly learn that he has a girl, a Jeep, and a dream. He says he wants to drive to Missouri with her, "just for the hell of it," he says. He asks which direction they're headed.

"That one," Les says, pointing east.

Chad nods and goes on about his plan to drive through the cornstalks in Kansas and explore the Ozark Mountains of Missouri for a few days. "Then," he breaks, "well, we'll just come home, maybe better off. Maybe more in love. Who knows."

"Yeah you will," says Les.

"Something she and I need to do, you know? You guys probably have girlfriends, I'm sure you know what I mean."

Aaron nods.

Joe walks into the room holding a plate full of grilled meat and another with a heap of tater tots.

"Guys," he says aloud, like about to give a speech, "welcome to Gunnison, and welcome to the adventures we'll talk about for at least the rest of this week. And may they never..." He pauses, searching for the right words. Chad starts laughing at the awkwardness, and Joe waves him off by saying, "may the adventures never cease!"

"Amen!" Chad yells, clapping his hands.

The next morning, Joe insists on buying smoothies for them from the place he works. "The perfect smoothie. Trust me. Your mind will explode with how good this will be." They pack and lean their bikes against a wall in the side yard. Joe is already in the car with his sunglasses on.

On the road, Joe says Chad works at a Sherwin-Williams paint supply store as an assistant manager, and that they work right across the street. Joe jokes about how Chad never visits and that he should, too, because he's right across the street. He explains that he, himself, is off the hook because nobody visits their friend who works at a paint supply store.

The café feels open and active. There is seating everywhere—against the walls, clustered in the center of the room, several outside.

"Get the granola express. Just trust me. Both of you should. You won't regret it."

"Alright, let's do it," Aaron says, excited. The inside of the shop smells like oranges.

Joe orders three.

Outside, the sky is new again. A golden sunrise has given way to tropical ocean blue, almost see-through, like glass. The three of them make small talk. Aaron is saying Gunnison reminds him of a college town in California called San Luis Obispo. "Slow mornings, overgrowth, cafés everywhere with young people working them."

"I might know the place," Joe says. "I have a brother out your guys' way. But," he says, yawning, "Colorado is better."

Back in the car, Aaron tells Joe they've had a great time. Joe gives a casual wave of his arm. "You kidding? This is life, guys, and if we can't share it together then what the hell's the point?"

"Agreed," says Les.

After readying to leave, Joe gives them each a strong hug. "Alright," he says, stepping back. "Now get the hell out of here. Go tour America."

Aaron waves as they ride away. Joe returns the gesture, his arm dropping as they turn left, and then right again where they come out at US Route 50. They point east now for the longest hill climb of the tour: Monarch Pass. *Every hill, every headwind, every flat tire. All of it has been training for this.*

Ten miles up the road a Jeep passes. There is a long, white arm hanging out the window. Then another arm pops out of the passenger side window. Both are waving.

"It's Chad!" Aaron yells.

They wave back spiritedly.

"And he's off on his adventure," Les says.

"Something poetic about getting to see them headed off like this, I think."

"A bunch of young guys pursuing their dreams. Touring the US by bike or taking a girl on a trip to Missouri," Les reflects.

The Jeep crests the next incline and drops down and out of sight.

They ride ten more miles of rising and falling road. They stop in front of a market within a valley just before a point where the road seems to spring upward and around with no apparent descent.

"This has to be it," Les says. "The moment we've been training for. This is it. Right here." He watches the hill. "We should eat," he says.

"Yeah I'm already starving."

As they stretch and chew on granola and apples, they don't speak. They are only bodies with internal thoughts. They've ridden hills before. They know cadence theories, how often to drink water, when to eat and when not to. They know how to keep from letting their muscles grow gelatinous, minds from getting lazy, bikes from diverging for a second into the road and then back to the shoulder.

But nothing theoretical really sticks when in the moment. No amount of schooling, book reading, seminars or support groups will compare to the body's instinct at the instant the gun goes off and the marathon begins. This sense of wild instinct carries the body up and over hills of every sort. *Instinct, prayer for favor and very little else*, Aaron thinks.

They begin.

They pull, pull and pull. Les works more on his cycling song. "Life has hill climbs, life has descents, both are from the hands of the Looooord..." he sings, Aaron smiling at every "Looooord," still without joining in.

In two hours, it is finished. At the top they cheer, high-five, hug and wave at tourists in sunglasses and sandals who look back at the valley they have climbed out of.

"Honestly, I thought this whole thing would have felt more epic. A little more inspirational or moving. I mean, dude, we just finished the craziest part of our ride," Aaron says.

"Right here, man. Right here. We've won. We just won! Woo!" Les screams. There at the summit, with his shirt off, Les begins singing the song again while lying on the summit's only patch of snow. By this time of year, it is a pile of black and brown peppered slush. "Both are from the hands of the Looooord..." he coos. "Both we will receive, and both we will endure. So ride on! Ride on, into the rising sun..."

It is 1:30. They sit together on the snow slush, taking their time. "We need a picture of this," Les says. "Our future families will need to know about this snow." Aaron stands and steadies the camera. Les begins making a dirty snow angel.

"That," Les says after, "is cold. And rough."

"That," Aaron jokes, "is what I could have told you."

"Ha."

"Hey, dude, so did you know you're twenty-four today?"

Les stops brushing twigs and ice from his reddened back. He stares at the ground. He looks as if he is about to recite Shakespeare. He looks at Aaron. "Dude you're right. It absolutely is my birthday." Les raises his arms: "Tour life! Monarch Pass on my birthday!"

The tourists with sunglasses and sandals look over again.

"Lunch is on me," Aaron says. "What sounds good? There is a gift shop that looks like it sells food."

"A breakfast burrito."

"A breakfast burrito?"

"My favorite food."

"Well then, a breakfast burrito it is."

What took two hours to climb takes twenty-five minutes to descend. It is twelve miles straight down the eastern side of the pass. They average low forties but feel as though they're going fast enough to start flying. The world is a blur of trees, road and air. They take a whole lane and no cars come from behind to pass.

At the bottom they reach the river again. They have in some way been following it since they reached Colorado. It has flown opposite them but, like them, has never stopped moving. The road back into civilization goes from greenery to ice and mountain to brown rock and red canyon walls, just like in Utah. The river is blue and clear, just like the sky.

Salida is hot. It is five in the evening by the time they arrive. They race to the other side of town for no other reason than that they are happy to be done with the divide. It is an ordinary town like so many they've seen already. There are no major attractions, just grocery stores, cafés, dry cleaners, restaurants.

Happy people thrive in the quaint and ordinary; busy and anxious people live in the loud and bustling. Salida must have happy people.

"I'd live here," says Les.

"Oh yeah?"

"Yeah. Ride every day. Hike in the mountains. Ski. Teach my kids to kayak in the river. I'm sure this town is full of active people."

"So, what's our host's name tonight?" Aaron says, changing the subject.

"Randy and Julie. Oh, and a kid named James."

"Cool."

"Said on their profile they've toured Europe."

"Very cool."

June 24, 2008

Life is a collection of sequential events, often unexpected, and character is how those events are met and lived with. Pregnancy, loss of a job, car accidents, job site catastrophes, natural disasters. We are not able to predict what comes of our lives, and we are not in control of what happens around us. We are, however, completely in control of how we decide to carry ourselves.

Julie meets Aaron and Les at her door and shows them where they can keep their bikes in the garage. There is a sign along the driveway that reads "Bikes Only," which is described by Julie as cute, but not all that practical. She says they park their car on it all the time. Inside the garage is a smaller bike on a repair stand.

"That's little James's bike," she says. "As soon as Randy is done building it we're going to let the little guy sprout wings." She stares at the ground. "I'm gonna miss riding around with him on the back of my bike."

"What a great thing to get to go on family bike rides though." Aaron says.

"You wouldn't necessarily realize it, but it really brings us three together. Well anyway, come on inside and get situated."

The house is small but unique. The bathroom sink has a giant mounted porcelain bowl that water pours into from the faucet. The shower is a block of shiny tile in the corner. No curtain, just a drain.

The kitchen is unfinished, which Julie mentions before they have time to notice. She is chopping fruit.

"I bet you guys are hungry."

"Always seems that way," Les says.

"That's touring," she says, nodding.

There are pictures of Randy, Julie and baby James in the living room. "Where is this one taken?" Aaron says, looking over.

"The Springs. We took James on a trip up there. A three day tour. Nothing fancy."

"He is a baby here, right?"

"He sure was. Once a touring family always a touring family." She smiles distantly and sets a large tray of fruit on the coffee table. "So, guys," she starts. "There is something you should be aware of."

"Oh?" Les says picking up a stick of celery and placing it between his teeth.

"Well, Randy isn't home from work yet. But, when he gets home I'm gonna need to tell him some bad, bad news.

"Oh?" Les says again, pulling the celery away.

"Yeah, I mean, just so you're aware, and so you know why we may be a little un-host-like this time around," Julie says, placing her hands together. "Well, his best friend was killed today."

Aaron and Les don't move. Aaron looks at Les and back at Julie. It is so sudden and surreal it feels like a scene from a movie. They say nothing, but sit in the might of all that Julie has said. She is sitting upright and proper, looking sorrowful but strong.

"He doesn't know yet, but when he gets in, I am going to tell him."

"Okay," says Aaron.

"Is there anything we can do?" says Les.

"You're so sweet," she says. "But no. Just know that I'm gonna send him right back out the door to the bar with his other friends, as they are all just finding out too. He loves being a host, trust me," she smiles. "But he won't be much of one tonight. Sorry about that."

"No apologies." Aaron says. "Just sorry to hear."

"Well, that's life, I guess," she says.

When Randy gets home he is promptly intercepted by Julie. They are talking quietly in the living room.

From their bedroom in the back of the house, Aaron stands up and moves into the backyard through a back door.

Outside, there is a tree, a fence on three sides, and a garden that has recently been planted. The yard smells like the Rockies in a sweet, piney way. The sky is still blue but with a tint of orange along the western edge. It is casting eastern shadows of trees, homes and parked cars all across Salida. It is 6:55.

Randy comes outside through a different door with a bag of trash in his hand.

"Hey, uhh..." Aaron says. "Can I give you a hand?"

The bag is large and Aaron reaches to open the lid.

"Sure, thanks. I'm Randy," he says and he puts out his hand. He starts to speak but stops. He nods and turns to go back inside.

Sleep comes as predictably as any night, which, to Aaron, feels slightly irreverent. In the morning, they stretch and pack, and wander into the kitchen holding their bags.

"Good morning," Randy says from the table. He is wearing a small, sky-blue bathrobe that might be Julie's, and holds a newspaper and a cup of coffee. "Hungry?" He says.

"Sure am," says Les. He brings up a chair.

"Your names are Aaron and Les."

"Yep," says Les, biting into a piece of toast.

"Not gonna lie. Had to reread the e-mail. Please man, sit," he motions to Aaron. "Have some oatmeal and fruit or whatever."

"Thanks," says Aaron.

"Coffee?"

"Yes please, thanks."

They talk about the route and Randy digs up an old tour map to indicate he and Julie's travels. If he is bothered by the news of his friend, he is hiding it well. He turns over his shoulder and looks at James who has been quietly playing in the living room. He is carefully constructing a tower out of his toys, lost in his own world.

"Fascinating, guys. Really incredible, this trip of yours," Randy says.

"Thanks. Thank you. We just started out as two guys with no experience and a dream," Les says.

"That's right, and now you're halfway."

"Halfway, man," Aaron says nudging Les. He feels the weight of the road in his legs; the pulse of their experiences inside his chest. *Maybe experiences like these are supposed to equip people to be able to give life back to each other.*

Randy digs up a set of front pannier racks from his garage. He says it won't do them any good without bags, but displacing the weight on the bike is key.

They tell him thanks and Aaron stuffs them into his panniers. Even in spite of his loss, Randy is a giver. It is in his bones.

The five of them—Randy, Julie, little James, Les and Aaron—pose for a picture. The flashing red light, and Les is scurrying back to the group.

Three. Two. One. Flash.

They shake hands and Julie gives hugs. Then, they wave as they ride away, their signature move. As in Gunnison, they wave until they are down the road and around the corner, out of sight.

GROANINGS & DEEP UTTERANCES

September 2007 — nine months until departure

Occasionally, but not always, coping mechanisms help people out of their troubles and direct them into the hands of something truly, wholly good. Some people cliché these mechanisms as bridges, stairways or stepping-stones, and sometimes metaphors like these do justice to the mechanisms being used. At the very least, merely turning something into a cliché is its own kind of coping. In my case, my mechanism had become my bike, and the cliché for it was something like a circuit breaker.

Often after a shift at the café I'd get on my bike and ride for a couple hours, knowing that the longer I'd stay away from home the longer I'd be able to avoid laying in bed, which would invariably mean being awake and thinking about the breakup. While riding, all I needed to do was throw the breaker and some sort of blackout would occur. When riding especially hard, this seemed to shut out most every worry. It would lift me from the earth for a while, and often when I'd land upon it again after finally returning home, I wouldn't have thought it was anything more than fifteen or thirty minutes. I was willfully blacking myself out, like purposely removing myself from existence for a period of time. The belief I carried was that if I threw the circuit breaker, then I would be released. Soon, however, I understood that something else might be at work.

On many summer nights, when the sun had finally left the sky and the heat upon the greater Los Angeles basin floor had risen and was dissipating into the cool night, the best time to ride was after 8 p.m.

My rubber tires whooshing across the pavement, the world becoming a peripheral blur, I often listened to a local band called the Cold War Kids. With fifty-two minutes or more to burn, I'd hit play and let singers Nathan Willett and Jonnie Russell sing me into oblivion. Their sulky, surly and often spontaneous-sounding tracks became a great comfort to me, and with time and several rides I'd grown to trust the way their chord changes and lyrics could make me feel. It became music by which to lift my soul.

Often, while whooshing down the road, I'd scream Willett's lyrics like hefty pleas into the night and wonder if they could, in some mysterious way, convey the hurt I was feeling to God. This desire for a kind of deeper language is quite common in some more charismatic Christian circles. Though it wasn't something I grew up being taught how to practice, I knew of friends who'd describe "groanings" or "deep utterances in the Spirit," often likened to speaking in tongues. The basic idea, as I understood, was that one's heart would be so overwhelmed with emotion for God that it would sometimes manifest itself in language incomprehensible to humans when uttered aloud. To God, however, it was entirely comprehensible. It was a language that went above the rules of languages, an intimate upwelling of adoration, amazement and love for the Creator.

As I cranked along those September nights, turning my pedals over and over, I wanted the Creator to know my anguish; as I swiveled on Cold War Kid's "Tell Me in the Morning" and barreled through the intersection of Mar Vista and Greenleaf in uptown Whittier, singing with Willett, I imagined being a modern-day David from the Psalms in the Bible, an honest poet who was no stranger to anxiety, torment and constantly calling out to God. As I pounded my legs into the asphalt on Lambert Road while making my way home, I hoped there was some way God could discern the cries of my heart through the lyrics I was singing so ardently.

For so long I'd been raptured away from reality by a girl, allowing her to determine my worth and what I signified to our world. I'd grown accustomed to being known foremost as her boyfriend. This sense of purpose gave me reason for going on about my life the way I did. My work schedule, sleep schedule, money-saving habits and my career path were a direct result of her being in my life. Jared once told me that when we allow something from the outside to direct our lives we are yielding to something we believe is a higher power than ourselves. If he was right, then my girlfriend had become my higher power; she had become my god.

Circuit breaker thrown, blackout in full effect, my neck directing my head to the stars— at the end of "Tell Me in the Morning," when only my panting breath and creaking gears could be heard in the few seconds before the next song would begin, I would long to hear the voice of God calling back. As the next song would begin, however, I would let my heart continue to sing. I would look down upon my bicycle, the coping mechanism that seemed to be directing me back into the hands of something truly and wholly good, and I would see God's provision; his subtle way of shutting out my fragile and easily distracted mind in order, perhaps, to woo me gently back to himself.

THE COST OF ACCEPTANCE

Life might be more like a search for identity than I'll ever realize. Being accepted by others, even at the expense of myself, has always been a large part of my identity — of who I am. In junior high and high school, this tended to mean I was a follower. For example, one night at work, when I was employed by a large chain bakery that made cinnamon rolls, my friend Joe convinced me to turn my hat and apron around and ride our skateboards through the mall. Somehow, we didn't get caught, but the manager at the Mongolian barbecue hut across the way ratted us out to our manager later. She pulled Joe and I aside individually. I'll never forget the look on her face. It wasn't of anger or confusion. It was disappointment.

She said, "Aaron, why would you ever agree to do something like that?" I'd shrugged and apologized, not knowing how deep the chord of identifying as one of Joe's mignons went.

Even after I'd bought my '74 Beetle with my hard-earned cinnamon roll money and decisively quit my job, I didn't understand at the time that I'd done this because I wanted to be seen as unpredictable and a little wild in the eyes of my friends. I'd called Joe and told him I'd quit and that we should roadtrip to Idyllwild in my new Bug listening to Creedence Clearwater Revival's "Fortunate Son" the whole way.

Come to think of it, Joe did think that was pretty cool. But after the Idyllwild weekend was over, after we'd driven back to Orange County and were readying ourselves to go back to school, I was back to being a follower. Only now without a job.

THE QUIET LEADER

When I got older I decided to start identifying as a leader, probably to compensate for all of the following I'd done. At some point growing up in my youth group and being a part of my cross-country team taught me that being a leader was far more noble than being a follower. It meant respect over making yourself look like an idiot; it meant your opinion was valid, enough for people to now start following you.

I became obsessed with being a leader. During the summer before my senior year in high school, my youth leader from church, Isaiah, asked me why I hadn't applied to go with the rest of the senior class on a trip to Denmark. I really looked up to Isaiah. He liked writing, Pearl Jam and literature, and I wanted his respect. So, I told him something I felt was worthy of respect. I said I hadn't prayed enough about going on the trip, and that if, eventually, God led me to go on the trip, that I'd go. "It's God's will, after all," I'd said. Isaiah looked at me, smiled and then said, "Aaron, you're not up against anyone to go on this trip. It's really not much of a decision, but I'm totally not going to force you to come. Just let me know if you change your mind, okay?"

A week later I did let him know. "Isaiah, I don't think God is calling me to do this. But thanks anyway." I wanted to feel his gaze of approval upon this wisdom-reeking statement I'd made.

"Alright, man," he said, smiling as before.

What he didn't know was that what I really wanted, even more than going on a trip to Europe with all my friends, was to become a cross-country captain. Around this time my identity was rather tightly wrapped around being a runner, and when I realized I couldn't be the best on the team, or even among the top seven (which was considered varsity), I'd turned my sights toward being the team's guru instead. Calm, careful, dedicated. Leader of stretches and tips on not getting cramps.

I trained hard that summer, and especially hard when my coach was watching. I was invigorated to hear him yell something like, "Way to push that hill, Green!" By the end of the summer, right around the time that my friends were getting back from Denmark, I went to cross-country camp in the Big Basin Redwoods with the elite from my team. We ran trails twice a day, ate nothing but carbs, and read Once a Runner by John L. Parker Jr.

around the campfire at night. On the last night, I knew my coach would be naming that year's team captain. This was a ceremony I'd been looking forward to all week. It was to be the validation that I'd craved for as long as I'd realized that becoming a leader meant I could stop being seen as a goof.

My coach stood, the flames of the fire reflecting in his eyes as he crossed his arms and looked thoughtful. "The quiet leader," he said, looking up and looking at me. "Aaron Green wants it. Come on up, Captain Green." I stood, feeling more proud at that moment than any other in my life. I walked to my coach, shook his hand and turned to face my team. But, before I could say anything, he continued to call out, to my horror, three additional captains. As we all stood side by side, facing the rest of our team, the honor I'd placed in being the team's most respectable individual began to shrivel.

So I'm just the quiet leader, I thought to myself. *Great.*

Tailwinds
(Colorado, Part Three)

Tailwinds are a cyclist's best friend. While headwinds slow a rider down due to blowing against the direction they're riding, tailwinds, in addition to providing no opposing resistance, will actually push a rider along from behind. The more upright a rider sits with a tailwind at his back, the faster he goes. Arms spread, chest out, eyes closed and a whisper of relief that says: "Thank you. Finally, yes. Thank you!"

It is around fifty miles from Salida to Cañon City. Joe from Gunnison pronounced it "Can-nun City," as did a man from a gas station where they filled up on water outside of Salida.

"Cannon City here we come!" Les yells, careening ahead, chest out, tailwinds pushing him along.

Cañon City is their halfway point, and they feel good finally putting more miles behind them, and with the tailwinds, they cover the first twenty miles in an hour, their muscles hardly feeling a difference.

"Halfway and it's only noon," Les says, locking their bikes to a sign in front of a diner. "It's been at least a week since we've been able to open up like that."

At a corner booth, while Les types out a new blog post, Aaron tries to peel back a few pages of *The Way of A Pilgrim*. Soon, he realizes that a little girl has taken great notice of them. She peers over her seat often to watch what they are doing.

Les looks up and waves.

She waves back and giggles. She is with her grandfather and when they rise to leave he asks, "Where you headed?"

"New York," Les says.

"Wow, New York, Rachel. Hear that?"

She nods, still fixated.

He holds her hand and says, "One day you'll be able to do that too."

She smiles and he waves to them as they exit.

"Hmm," Les says. "We can inspire the generations."

"Never considered that."

"Kids remember things."

"Yeah, but most probably don't think about crazy things like riding a bike across the United States," Aaron says, plainly.

Les holds his chin for a moment before looking up at Aaron. "But don't they?"

Les had sent an e-mail out to their next Warm Showers hosts, Jasper and Midge, a retired principal and homemaker, and as they are readying to leave Jasper has already written back:

> *Hey Guys,*
>
> *Just head on up. You'll find me on my bike too. I need to get out anyway, so let's meet at the bug museum. See you then!*
>
> *-Jasper Hendrickson*

"The bug museum."

"The what?"

"Probably giant flies and ladybugs at the entrance."

"There better be."

The heat sets in. *The body is deceiving. It feigns strength when it has adventure to devour. It is like an old car that, with good oil, will run for miles and miles, but when it gets low everything acts up.* They are in an eastern valley of the Rockies and temperatures rival the desert in California. Mirage-like heat waves seem only a hundred feet away, but as they crank, the road warmly swimming underfoot, cooking their water bottles, the waves remain in the same place.

"Dude, this sucks."

"I know," Aaron calls back.

"This definitely isn't the Rockies anymore. I mean the hills. Look at the hills now," Les says. He is right. They are green, but on the verge of beige. There is dirt the color of khaki, and instead of trees, there are bushes and brush.

Soon, Les falls back and before long can be heard taking a phone call. Aaron waits, coasting along.

"Great— No, yeah, we're great with that— Okay, see you soon. Thanks." A pause. Then Les calls up to Aaron: "So, he wants to know how we feel about taco salad."

"Oh man."

"Yeah, that's what I said," Les says.

"Hey, Les!" comes the voice of an oncoming rider. He wears a jersey with the American flag and rides a bike with a rack and cooler he has rigged on top, just like Les's. It is Jasper Hendrickson.

"Jasper!" Les yells back.

"Guys, we're still fifteen miles away!" He says as he moves to their side of the road. "I knew it was you, though. See that ridge up there?" He pants. "I came up on it and waited until I saw you. Then you came and I started down."

The ridge is another hill they'll have to climb.

"Hey, you guys like taco salad?"

Aaron thinks about how this is the first question Jasper has though to ask them and smiles.

"Yeah we do!" says Les attempting to match his enthusiasm.

"Great, hang on." He pulls out a phone and hands them each a water bottle from a cooler he has mounted to the back of his bike. "Hey, Midge. Midge—yes, yes they are here and they want the taco salad. Yes—what's that? No, another hour. Yes—okay. Bye."

Aaron feels for another hour in his rubberized muscles and comes up empty.

"Taco salad it is! Ready?"

They ride fast. Jasper leading is fortunately like following a wall that breaks through the wind. They hardly notice the ridge. They careen down the other side and into the southern outskirts of Colorado Springs. The city is pushed up against the eastern mountains. It is quaint in a way that feels peaceful, yet large, and in a way that shrugs, acknowledging generations of stories.

Jasper doesn't let up. His cyclometer reads twenty miles per hour on the flats and he is casual, steady. Les and Aaron relish the opportunity to not have to trade off leading. Instead, they follow their newest friend's persistent pace. His American flag jersey freely waving ahead.

The Hendricksons live in a one-story home with two bedrooms. "Never needed anything bigger," Jasper says as he points around. They hadn't asked but he seems content to share this bit of information. He tells them he owns a truck, too. There is an apple tree and a clothesline out back. Grass and a tool shed. Nothing more, but nothing less.

Midge is waiting on the back patio with a glass of iced tea. When she rises to greet them, she stands tall and casually. Jasper does all the explaining.

"Saw 'em out there from the ridge. You know the ridge, Midge."

"I do." She smiles at them.

"Right after the bug museum I knew they had to be just around the corner, so I kept going. Then there they were! I swung down, rounded them up and we headed home. But you know, they mentioned your taco salad a few times and I'll bet that's what got 'em here." He looks over and winks.

Jasper pours them all a glass of iced tea without asking if they want any. Then, motioning toward a salad bowl full of taco salad, he says, "Look at that guys, better dig in before I eat it all. Whew, what a workout. I did thirty today, but from Salida I bet you guys did about a hundred."

"Did we?" Aaron asks and looks at Les, who nods and begins filling his plate.

"Well I hope this is enough. Really now, please make yourselves completely at home. Anything you want, food, books, a ride somewhere. Just say it."

"Thank you," Les says.

"Oh, and I have this friend, Rick Lunde. Pronounces it *Loon-dee*. Isn't that something?" He laughs. "Anyway, you should really stay at his house too, if you can. He'd get a kick out of hosting. Anyway, so he and I have done some touring too. The farthest we've toured was from San Diego to Colorado Springs. Doing what you young guys are doing but in three segments. San Diego to the Springs, then this summer the Springs to the Mississippi River. Then, if we're not too old, the Mississippi clear to the Atlantic."

Jasper then asks about the tour; about which places were most difficult. Les says Arizona, which leads Jasper into his stories of people he met while touring in Arizona, too. "The strangest people live there," he says. "But, I'll tell you what, you never know who you're gonna meet on the road, ain't that right guys?" He nudges Aaron with his elbow.

Around nine o'clock, when the day of riding and the taco salad have had enough time to digest and cool their weary bodies back to normalcy, Jasper laughs and says they look wasted.

"Couldn't get an hour of work outta you two now," he says, and they all laugh, even Midge.

Jasper shows them to the spare room in the back of the house. "So, what kinds of things are you reading?" he says.

"Kerouac, Donald Miller," Aaron says. "But honestly there hasn't been much time to really dig into anything since the trip began."

Jasper nods, and then says that his house gets boring and so if they want to read his books he's got plenty that he'd love them to explain to him. "I love reading but don't always get it.

That's okay though. I do it because I love it. Well," he says. "Tailwinds, gentlemen. Sleep as long as you like."

Their room is blue with a large mirror and two air mattresses, which they raise and lean against the wall. They roll their sleeping bags out where the air mattresses were. Something about sleeping on the ground feels more natural.

"Hey, Aaron."

"Yeah?"

"I want to be Jasper Hendrickson some day."

"Ha-ha, I knew you were going to say that."

"No really."

"Okay," Aaron laughs as he imagines Les in an American flag jersey.

"Well, tailwinds, brother."

"Indeed. Tailwinds."

When they wake it is 10 a.m. In the living room, when they come in rubbing their eyes, Jasper drops his paper and says, "Well, I said sleep as long as you want and you took me at my word."

"Pancakes here for you boys. Kept them warm," Midge says from the kitchen.

"They're delicious, really. If you'd have slept any longer Midge and I were just gonna eat them and send you to the store for more."

"Ha," says Les. "Thank you." He sits.

"So I had to tell Rick your story. I couldn't wait so I called after you went to bed. Long story short he'd love to have you over tonight. What do you think?"

"Well," Aaron starts, looking at Les. "We were hoping to rest all day today—"

"See the sights, drink coffee, update the blog, maybe go to church tomorrow," Les says.

"Oh, that's perfect. Let me just call Rick now. He'll love to take you tonight. He and Iris both, right Midge?"

She nods.

"Hell, they'll take better care of you than we will!" He laughs

Midge rolls her eyes, and then sincerely says, "I know you've got some wash, guys. Just leave it right by the machine and I'll throw it all in."

"Oh no, you don't—" Aaron starts.

"No, no. I know it's all stuffed in those bags somewhere. Raised three boys now," looking at Jasper.

He winks at them, his phone to his ear.

"Won't be any bother at all. It would be my pleasure to help," she continues.

"Well, sure," Les says. "Thank you."

Aaron is quiet and stirs his pancakes in syrup.

Jasper now has Rick on the phone. "Yeah—mhmm. They do. They want—what's that? No, they—yes. Hell, man, just listen! They even want to go to church with you and Iris. How about that?"

Jasper hangs up and brings out his maps. He explains where they've come in from. "Salida, and Monarch Pass before that no doubt."

Les nods.

"Telluride?" He asks slowly, looking up as if he were just reading a crystal ball.

Les nods again.

"Yep, yep," Jasper says slowly. "Came in through Cortez and before that Monument Valley. No cyclist would have missed that. How'd you like it?"

"Beautiful," says Aaron.

"Camped under the stars alongside roads and rows of buttes. Our bikes could have leaned up against them we were so close," Les says.

"Oh that valley," Jasper says. "Where the earth shoots up to the sky and just sits there looking out at everything."

"Exactly," says Les.

After breakfast they leave their bags in the guest room and jump into Jasper's F-150. It is the first time they've left their belongings somewhere since they started. They are like normal tourists now, headed out to explore the city.

Streets in the Springs feel ordinary, just like home. There are familiar chain restaurants and bulk grocery stores. Jasper talks about his sons. "They've accomplished a lot at their ages, just like you two," he says.

The road is soft—after riding their bikes on so much asphalt, it feels as if they are rolling along upon a bed of thick grass. It feels good to be in a vehicle, almost hypnotic. It feels good to feel as if they are home again.

Jasper drops them off at a coffeehouse called Agia Sophia. From there he says to go up to Garden of the Gods in the west. "Just beautiful up there. Even more than your Monument Valley." He waves and pulls away.

"Let's come back for coffee," Les says. "Kinda want to explore the garden first."

They ride their unburdened bikes, their frames shaking between their legs because of the lack of weight upon their racks. They roll along slowly and comment on how awkward it feels, almost like learning to ride a bike all over again.

Garden of the Gods is a desert scape built into the mountains and entirely unpopulated. Purple trees and rock formations lie in wait for tourists to come stand upon them and eat lunch beneath them. There is a serenity, a holiness about the stillness in the air. Nothing moves. God could be walking around and watering the plants somewhere deep within.

In what appears to be an old bedroom that is now fitted from top to bottom with books, Aaron suddenly says, "Wisdom love!" He points at Agia Sophia's logo on his cup.

"Definitely a Greek phrase, that's right," Les says. "Love wisdom," he says.

A moment passes. And then they both seem to say in unison: "The love of wisdom."

"Our Greek language classes weren't a complete waste after all," Les says, looking around.

There appears to be more wall space covered with books in cases than there is blank wall space. There are old titles by Dickens and Shakespeare. There are resources: dictionaries, almanacs, encyclopedias and Bible commentaries. Agia Sophia is basically a small library.

"This is the kind of vibe I'd want for my coffee shop," Aaron says. He breathes through his coffee. It swirls around in the air.

"Small spaces, books, coffee. Stock plenty of tea for me," says Les.

"Dark walls. Maybe a book check-in, check-out system."

"A library."

"Well, no, I've never wanted to do that."

"A book-borrowing house."

"Yeah, something like that."

"With coffee."

"And pastries," Aaron adds.

"Pastries and brownies, and an upstairs with different kinds of rooms. Reading rooms."

"People can come and use the space for whatever studious acts they want. Open to the community."

"So like a small, kind of independent community center?"

"No. But in a way maybe. I just want to create space for people to come and be. Like a refuge. A place for them to be themselves and to be able to work on creative things."

Les nods and closes his eyes for a few seconds. "Well, can I help build it?"

"Can you? I'd be offended if you didn't."

Jasper is around by three to pick them up again. "Well, how was the day, gentlemen?" He says after getting out. His F-150 is still running and his hazard lights are flashing.

"Fantastic," Les says, heaving his bike over the truck bed.

"Loved it, Jasper," Aaron says. "Great recommendation on both places. We got a ton done."

Jasper drives them to his place where they collect their bags, and Midge has nicely folded their washed clothes and stacked them next to their sleeping bags. They load the truck again, this time with all of their belongings, and are off to Rick and Iris's.

"Hey, guys," Jasper says in a somber tone, his hands across the wheel. "You don't know it but this has been such fun to have you. Something so enlivening about having you. Brings up an old guy's spirit and reminds him that he can do incredible things, too." He looks back at Aaron who nods at him. "Just slower, of course."

They all laugh.

Jasper winds down back roads, hugging corners and accelerating into turns that explode into afternoon hillside masterpieces. *This is colorful Colorado.*

Iris greets them at the door, smiling. She very politely welcomes the three of them into her home.

"Tea?" She asks.

Jasper says, "No, not right now. Probably keep me up. I got a lot of sleeping to do later on tonight." Aaron also says no but Les accepts. They four make small talk, learning that Rick met Iris while serving in Japan with the military. The Eastern decorations, pastel and off-white, many of which are ceramic cats, seem to make more sense now.

"Where is Rick anyway?" Jasper says.

"Oh, Jasper, you know Rick. Always out and about somewhere. Last I saw he was gardening."

They all hear the door creak slowly open and a man of about sixty, wearing a sun hat, gardening knee pads and Crocs and holding a watering can, walks in. "Hello, gentlemen," he says, setting down his watering can. "I'm Rick. This here is Iris and we are happy to have you."

"Oh, they've already met Iris, Rick," Jasper says. "Had some tea and have been chatting about you here for a while."

"Oh. Alright then. Guys, this is your house tonight and until you decide to leave tomorrow. Bathroom is that way, down the hall. Your room is across from it. I may be scarce this evening. I'm singing a hymn at the church tomorrow. Jasper," he says, turning to his friend.

Jasper looks up.

"Will you be there at church tomorrow?"

"Going out of town to visit my son actually. Sorry, Rick."

"Well, it sounds like Jasper won't be there, guys. But you're more than welcome to join us for church."

"Which hymn will you be singing?" Les says.

"A broken version, compliments of me, of 'His Eye Is on the Sparrow.'"

"Oh, yes, I know it well," Les says and smiles.

"Very good," Rick says nodding. "I'll be getting cleaned up now. And Jasper?"

"Yeah, Rick?" Jasper's hands are in his pockets, rustling change and keys.

"Thanks for sharing the touring cyclists here with us."

"Anytime." Jasper smiles and winks at them.

"Alright then," Rick says as he leaves the room.

"Well, gentleman," Jasper says, turning to face them. "I don't usually have inspiring words to give to people. Not really my strong suit. I'm more of a giver of resources and good conversation. A friend more than anything." He stops and seems to find peace in something he has decided to say. "You two have been like sons to me and Midge. I mean, even in the short while. And you will to Rick and Iris, of course. But Rick'll never tell you that." He laughs. "Anyway, just remember that."

"We will," Les says, reaching to shake his hand. "We'll never forget it."

June 26, 2008

> *As Jasper pulled away tonight in his truck he reminded me of Larry from Redlands, and Dad back in Corona. Here's another man with responsibility on his plate but adventure in his heart. Even with a desire to get out and enjoy the road, it can be difficult to break away and do it. But its rewards have to be invaluable; the road, on a bike, is a place for adventures to become eternal again. Jasper knows it, and we're getting to know it too.*

Rick sings with a kind of reverent abandon, almost like a child, as if his former military titles and reputation didn't matter. As if his role in management at his store could take a backseat to this opportunity—this very moment, and all the other moments in his life at church and at home in his garden—when he got to be a kid again. His eyes are glued. His face a painting, solemn and still. His grasp around the microphone, steady, contemplative even, as though he'd spent an hour in his study at home rehearsing even how to receive the mic, how to hold it as he'd begin, when he'd come to sing and how he'd place it back on its stand when he was done. Rick is a man with calculations in his mind and appreciation flowing out of his heart.

The minister is easily half Rick's age. Stilly, Rick is more than excited to introduce his pastor to his cycling visitors. Tom is his name, and his witty sermon and casual demeanor seem to suggest that he is educated but not bloated by it. He has blonde hair and glasses too big for his face. His belly shakes when he laughs.

"So, what are you guys really doing anyway?" he says.

"Just out taking a bike ride," Les says.

"And you what, got to the desert in California, looked around, and said, 'Man, we have to keep going?'"

"No—" Aaron starts.

"Yes, exactly," Les says.

"Valiant. Courageous even," Tom says, looking amazed. "So, from here you're just going to ride through Colorado or what? 'Cause there ain't anything past this. Unless you really do like the desert. Eastern Colorado is almost post-apocalyptic."

Aaron hadn't heard anyone describe Colorado as anything but incredible, anything but inescapably ridden with fantasy and wonder, anything but just short of God's own backyard.

"New York," Les says. His arms are across his chest as he is studying Tom the minister.

"Even better," he says. "Eeeeeven better." He seems to ponder all that riding from California to New York might imply. He is holding his chin. "So, then what? You've conquered America as you ride across the bay in the Staten Island ferry. You kiss the earth, high-five a stranger, get a drink or whatever you enjoy having, and then... Well, then what?"

"Never really got that far I guess," Aaron says. "Guess we'll decide what's next when we get there."

"A true traveler," Tom says, slapping Aaron on the arm. "So, you know you won't be able to put this fire out anymore, right?"

Aaron looks at him, confused.

"The ride?" Les says.

"Right. The ride. You'll be telling this story for the rest of your lives, and maybe you'll get bored of it, I have no idea. But, life is short, as you may or may not know, and there's only tiny windows for second and third chances."

"Bike rides, you mean. More of them," Les says.

"Bike rides, hikes, car rides. Whatever, man. The point is you've had a taste and you'll go clear to New York. I know it. Couple of young guys like you. Little can stop a young man with a big enough appetite. It's a fire that can only be appeased by buckets of more adventure. More of these trips. Just wait, you'll see. You'll want nothing to do with it after you're done. But give it a few months. A year maybe. You'll be hooked. You'll want nothing more than to be on the road again."

"On the road again," Aaron repeats.

"Tom," Les says. "Do you do this kind of stuff too?"

He nods. Smiles. "Look at me, though. Sure, I take adventures, you better believe it. But not every one of them is active. I mean, I'm fat." He laughs. "But sure, mine are adventures, but how I like them. Specific to me."

"Yeah. I get it. Not every voyage is a trip through the sea," Les says.

"Hey, we've got a regular poet here! Did you want to speak to the congregation next week, man?"

Rick and Iris are quiet types. They are proper. They prefer organic blueberries and yogurt pancakes to traditional meals. They enjoy one cup of coffee each in the mornings, but nothing more.

After breakfast Les asks to get a picture with them in their Japanese garden, which they agree to. Afterward, they hug and then Aaron and Les depart, leaving another fond memory of people who'd treated them like their own.

The hot road makes more mirage-like waves a mile away from Colorado Springs. Images seem to float in the distance, beckoning: *Come. This way to the unknown. It's hotter than hell out here. But come. Don't stop now. There is still much to see.*

"Aaron," Les says slowly, riding up alongside. There is asphalt rolling like black water beneath them.

"Yeah?"

Les stares out at the brown, eastern Colorado country. They have all the time in the world out here. "We were like sons to these people." He lets these words fall from his mouth as if he didn't know they were there. As if he'd just made a surprising discovery.

Aaron looks over.

"In Colorado, to Edgar. To all of them," Les says. He looks down at his hands steadying his bike. "One thing I'm realizing on this trip is how fortunate we are."

Aaron nods.

Les sits up straight. "We are like the bicycling sons of America on this trip!"

The highway they ride is typical. They turn south out of Colorado Springs and then east again, the Rocky Mountains at their backs, and now the roving color brown all around. Dirt is today's pastures. Dirt, empty road and dead trees.

They fill up on water at a spigot outside a gas station on the outskirts of a town called Boone. It is around seven in the evening and the sun is lingering along the Continental Divide. The mountains are silhouettes. Telluride, Gunnison, Salida, Colorado Springs, all memories now. Only this, the town of Boone, in the middle of nowhere, where even trees refuse to reside, is real. The air feels empty, as though the mountains behind them are a vacuum that pulls life and sounds into their midst. Boone perpetuates the idea in Aaron's mind that life was not meant to exist where other people have chosen not to reside.

They set up camp past a row of unlit houses and a closed-down convenience store.

"Eerie, right?" says Les.

"What—this place? Really eerie. Freaking eerie. Almost weird, and a little sketchy."

While they sleep, a train passes in the night. Otherwise, they aren't disturbed.

In the morning they eat leftover yogurt and granola pancakes from Rick and Iris and peel off pieces of bread from a day-old loaf they bought before leaving town.

The sun is up and the land is knowable again. They watch the road quietly. They wait. Nothing happens. No cars pass.

TELL ME WHY YOU'RE HERE
(PART TWO)

September 2007 — nine months until departure

Alex took a moment to read his notes. With his legs crossed and his head tilted toward the ground, he looked as if he was about to ask me a question but was trying to find the right words.

I waited. I took a deep breath of potpourri-scented counseling center air and could faintly hear classical music playing in the lobby. Both were distantly comforting sensations to me, like being at a grandmother's house that I barely knew.

"Okay, so let's talk a little about the cross-country bike ride," Alex said. "When are you going?"

"This summer, after I finish school."

Alex nodded. "Tell me about Les's challenge for you to ride a bike across America."

"Well, it was actually my idea. I guess I'd begin describing the situation—my situation—feeling as if I were constantly pushing a stone to the top of a hill." I pantomimed pushing a stone upward. "Since I'd seen it roll back down the same way so many times, I guess I'd come to expect that to happen, just like any other time, the night we decided to do the ride. But instead, my buddy Les took that stone and pushed it over the other side of the mountain so that I couldn't do it anymore."

Alex looked confused. "Care to explain that for me?"

"Sure," I said. "So, it's a metaphor I adopted from a story I heard in my philosophy class about a guy named Sisyphus. I remember reading it and feeling a vague connection to my experience, even if I was stretching the metaphor considerably. In short, as punishment for a crime, Sisyphus was condemned to ceaselessly rolling a rock to the top of a hill, only to let it roll back down and to start over. The belief was that there was no worse punishment than pointless labor."

"So, you're feeling like what you've felt since the breakup is laborious, or pointless?"

"Well, I knew I felt some sort of punishment in losing my two best friends, and I'd felt like my toiling certainly served little point. I was the one who had to deal with losing them and all of the hopelessness and fear that came with it, not them. So in some ways, almost every day I'd roll my stone up my hill and watch it roll right back down."

Alex still looked confused.

I tried to clarify. "It was less of a punishment, and this is where I diverge from the Sisyphus story, because I knew that by complaining audibly and constantly reexamining my situation with my friends that I could keep feeling sorry for myself. As my stone would lumber down the hill I think I secretly hoped people would sympathize with me."

Then I told Alex the story about sitting at the café with Jared and Les that night during the summer when I was piling up complaints with my torn-up straw shards. I told him about the crazy look in Les's eye and about how he is an organizational freak meets spontaneous thrill-seeker meets pastor.

This was the most confused I'd ever seen Alex look.

"Just trust me," I said. "Les is exactly how that sounds, and only Les can embody such a combination."

To this, Alex shrugged and seemed content.

"So actually," I continued, "about the bike ride, in the moment I said something like: 'I don't know man; that sounds kind of crazy.' To which Les just asked me why it sounded crazy, and I could see that all excuses for not going were out the window with him. But I think, even more, I could see what he was doing, and it felt good and right then because I could see that someone was willing to come and do something with me. And for me. Really, I think we could have hiked down to the beach, or road-tripped in a car somewhere, or whatever. What we would do wasn't the point. The point was that he committed to doing something with me at all."

Alex wrote something down on his notepad and then turned the cap clockwise on the butt of his pen. "So, why do you think his commitment to you was so important?"

"Well, I mean, I think having anyone commit to doing something with you is pretty selfless and remarkable. He was willing to forfeit his entire summer, not to mention training for the whole year prior with me."

"So his selflessness then? That's what you find so great about his commitment."

"Yeah. I think so." I said. "But, to be frank," I looked up.

He nodded and sat back, his expression the same.

"When I say the point was that Les committed to doing something with me, I mean that for me, knowing I had a buddy willing to walk in my shoes, and then to take me the extra mile, was most significant. I mean, I pray for strength all the time, but waking up every morning prior to Les's challenge, always feeling one step behind, was getting really tiresome. I was beginning to wonder where God's help would come from, or if I believed it would come at all. So, yes, Les was selfless. But even more, he was my ally. He sacrificed doing whatever he wanted to do next summer just so that I could get better. That seemed his real motivation; that was really what he was doing, even if I didn't know it right away. But now, I think I know."

"What is that that you know now?"

"Well, not to sound dramatic, but I think I'm seeing that trusting friends again is possible."

Alex nodded and wrote on his notepad again.

XANGA

After high school and into my first year of college, I was working an entry-level warehouse job shipping industrial-grade light bulbs all around the country. It was the typical college job—it met my needs and gave me something to do. But otherwise, I was bored and always on the lookout for new hobbies. I started playing the bass with my friends in The Jacaranda Jam. I hunted for sweet finds at thrift stores. I usually went barefoot around school and I grew my hair really long. Most of these hobbies were secretly, if not overtly, meant to make a statement, because when you strive for other's good opinions of you, you're always making a statement. This was my real hobby, and I gave a lot of effort to it.

One of my other great hobbies was blogging. At the time, Facebook was still an infant and really only something you could use if you went to a university somewhere. People found other ways to blog and socialize online, though, mostly through Myspace or Xanga. This was before Twitter too, so people were free to write all kinds of things at various lengths.

My Xanga profile changed all the time, especially when I saw someone else's I liked. I'd fly over and attach myself to their words for a while before flying back into my own space and making an edit.

The one thing I was really great at was finding people. It was amazing how socially productive I could be from behind a computer screen. I "followed" hundreds of bloggers, establishing the allure of being the kind of guy who had a lot of friends. I lived for those people to follow me back and visit and comment on my blog as I did on theirs.

SHE'S A BRICK

On one particularly slow day while working at the light bulb warehouse, I came upon the Xanga page of a girl I recognized from school. She was a year younger than me, and she always wore low-top Converse shoes with thick plaid skirts and band t-shirts, all of which I was a fan of.

Her Xanga background was light green with pink accents, and the banner read: "she's a brick." The first time I read it I finished the line, singing aloud to myself, "HOOWWSE," mistaking it for a reference to a song by the late '70s funk and soul band, The Commodores (which, come to find out, it wasn't).

This Xanga banner could have been a warning sign. But even if it was—even if the phrase "she's a brick" was meant to be read as a subtle caution, an indicator of the rough-ness of the metaphorical walls that she'd built inside of herself, alerting me to keep back or at least to tread lightly, I was still just a kid traveler passing through. She might be built of brick, but at least she was a house. I was unaware of any danger and filled with hope by the warm romantic possibilities I thought I might come to find inside.

I often wonder what life would have been like had I decided not to keep reading. If I'd have received an important phone call, or if my boss had walked in and told me to go do something other than sit around reading crap on the internet; if I would have just kept scrolling through other Xanga profiles, skipping right over hers, then I might have gone on to miss something truly life changing.

That is to say, I would have missed the hardest, most heartbreaking breakup of my life. I don't blame her, or myself, or anyone else. I had no way of knowing how deeply sunken her childhood foundation was. I couldn't have known about any of her traumatic experiences that taught her to build walls inside of herself for safety. How, over the next thirty-three months of my life, could I know that I'd come to be enamored by her, taken by my own need to give, and by giving, to garner identity as someone's savior and in the end only find myself heartbroken with my fingernails filled with blood-red brick dust having barely scratched her surface?

But I was smitten by her type. I hummed "Brick House"—*duuun duun duun dun dun duuuun!*—to myself and started to read her latest post. She was fiery, using the words "posh scenesters" and "angsty." She wrote about literature and music, about her lame parents, and playing sports "with all the boys" at work. Soon I found myself finished with a month's worth of her posts. Then two months. Four. Six. A year. A week of my life had gone by and I knew her affinity for Asian people, that her word "juicy" meant something like cute, or adorable, or lusciously cute and adorable.

And then I knew I needed to meet her.

City Boys
(Colorado, Part Four)

Colorado State Highway 96 leads east with a slight bend north. Just as the road leading into Boone, this road offers the eye only scarcity.

Les pulls a picture into the camera, and while looking at it and calmly moving along the middle of the street, straddling and weaving in and out of dotted yellow lane paint, he says, "If we carbon-copied this picture here twelve billion times and posted it on the blog every day a million times, then our fans would know what this road feels like."

"Ha," Aaron says looking up. "Our fans?"

"Yeah, our viewers and cheerleaders. Our people who anxiously await reading our stories."

"I guess I thought 'fans' was a funny way of putting it. Like we're athletes on a sports team. Or like we're important enough to have fans."

"Best damn athletes in the world!" Les suddenly yells into the open air, his arms off his bike and spread wide. His palms are exposed to the sun and his chest is out. After a moment he says, "I love this, man." Then he yells: "I love touring the United States of America!"

They ride in silence for a while. "Can you believe that we get to do this?" Les says.

Aaron nods, knowing Les's excitement, but not sure how to show it in a way that feels as genuine as screaming aloud. Even if he did, he didn't have the energy to match Les.

Forty miles farther and Colorado is quickly coming to a close.

One can always revisit and try it all again, Aaron thinks. He glances back to try to pinpoint the Springs, where Jasper, Midge, Rick and Iris live. *There is always the future, but even still, the hours we shared with them will never be replaced. We can relive nothing, only remember. Everything is fascinating, boring, terrifying, exciting and everything else the first time around. It is the unknown that we pack our bags to see. And why? What draws us to having original adventures? Why do we crave the road when we know it will never be like it was before? Maybe, it is because we hope each time we go that it will be just a little better.*

Olney Springs, Colorado, is an empty town like Boone. There is one main drag with residential streets on either side that poorly hide behind sporadically placed trees attempting to act as partitions.

"Want to top off water?" Les says.

"Good call."

There is a diner with green trim and a long, wide concrete porch. A waitress waves at them as they park and peer in. They wave back and Les is quickly inside, asking about where to fill up water bottles.

She points toward the back and then smiles toward Aaron, who is stretching on the porch and noticing the only two patrons at a table who, staring at him, look as though they've just seen the president walk by. Aaron waves to them too. One of them wears a cowboy hat. He gently lifts it, sets it down and turns back to his friend at the table. They exchange glances for the next few minutes, their heads turning and eyes passing back upon the window from time to time.

Les has four bottles in his arms and he pushes through the screen door with his hip.

"Hey," comes a small voice somewhere behind them.

They look at each other.

"Hey you, bikers," it comes again.

They walk to the end of the porch and see that they are being confronted by a group on bicycles. They don't wear cycling jerseys and they aren't carrying water bottles either. None wear helmets.

"Who are you?" says the leader.

"I'm Les, and this is Aaron," he says, matter-of-factly.

"Oh," says the leader. "Where you come from?"

"California," Aaron says.

At this, their eyes widen. They look at each other. They aren't quiet when they talk to each other about the two mysterious men in front of them.

"We've never been to Cal-eh-forn-ya," one says. "Not even really sure where it is."

"Where you guys from?" Les says.

"Olney," says the one to the leader's right. "Just up there, behind the trees."

"Yeah, we all from here. 'Cept him," says another, who points at one in sandals and a blue T-shirt. He has been disinterested at the group's find.

"And where's he from?"

"Denver," says the leader. "I ain't never been there neither. Have you?"

They shake their heads at the group who, it would seem, are getting bored. One begins pedaling in circles, and another follows. Soon, they are riding around the porch, passing Les and Aaron and staring. The one from Denver has the best bike and doesn't make eye contact. The leader has yet to move.

"Where you going?"

"New York," says Les, pulling back a drink of water.

"New York!" the leader yells.

The rest of the gang yell with him, one letting out a WHOOPPEEEE!

Questions then come flying. Why are you going to New York? Where is your family? Are you guys friends? What does your teacher think? Are you guys in school? Did you guys drop out of school? How far is California? Is it farther than New York?

The gang is rolling around and around.

Aaron and Les shrug.

The gang rides battered BMX bikes, some without air pressure in their tires. Two appear to be on their sister's bikes.

"Hey, you guys ever plan to take a trip when you get older?" Les says.

"I do. I plan to go to Denver," says the leader. "M'dad is gonna take me."

Les reaches into his bag and pulls out five of their business cards and places one in each of their hands like candy on Halloween.

They study the yellow photo paper and black writing.

"What's it say?" The one in sandals asks.

"It's our blog," Aaron says. "Know what that is?"

They look at each other.

"Have you ever written down on a piece of paper something you did? Maybe it was at school, or maybe at home?"

They nod and share every story they can think of, cutting each other off, trying to outdo the last guy's story.

Finally Aaron breaks in. "Well, have your parents take you on the internet. When you're there, tell them to type these letters in on these cards. Then tell them to read to you. You'll hear all about us. You might even read about New York."

They are all chattering again, and soon they are riding circles again, business cards in hand and cheers coming out of their little chests.

The gang waves at Aaron and Les as they start to leave. The littlest one is still riding circles in the diner driveway. Soon, they too are specks on the horizon.

"Olney Springs," Les says. "A place to grow up."

Just west of the Kansas border is a town called Eads. It has six or seven blocks, easily twice the size of the last three towns they've seen, put together. There is a county courthouse building right in the middle with the greenest grass since Telluride. Sycamores hang like giants above the building. There is a park with public restrooms, a row of tall bushes and a lawn big enough for a soccer game.

"We're definitely stealth camping this lawn tonight," Les says.

It is odd how clean, orderly and seemingly vacant Eads is. Cars roll through, but infrequently enough to support the thought that Eads might be a façade for some kind of regional cult. This would explain the lack of people and the beautiful greenery, and the fact that none of the courthouse windows can be seen through.

The next morning it is raining. Aaron is first to wake to the rhythmic sound of water grazing and then splattering across the tent. It is 6:30. *Rain in eastern Colorado, in the summer, in the middle of nowhere. Weird, but maybe this is how everything stays so green?* He rubs sleep from his face. The sun is out, peeking through the screen at the top of the tent. The rain, though, is landing on the tent horizontally.

Suddenly, the rain ceases. He unzips the tent, peers out the front and sees work boots, dirty work pants. He hears the sound of a man chuckling. Outside the tent there are no clouds, only golden light glistening through the leaves of dampened trees above. The man is staring at him, still chuckling. When Aaron looks up, the man looks away and continues working, wrapping a hose and switching off a sprinkler at its terminal. *A sprinkler.*

"Today might see a hundred miles," Aaron says looking back into the tent.

"Finally," Les says. "Man, we're due. We've needed this kind of distance for a while."

"Kinda got a little backed up with all of the hill riding in Colorado," Aaron says, blankly.

"We might have to hitchhike again unless we want to do hundred-twenty-plus days for the next two weeks," Les says casually.

Aaron rolls his eyes and peers across the landscape. There is a thin, blue sign along the road no bigger than that of a call box that reads:

WELCOME TO KANSAS.

PRAYER, PIPES & EX-LOVES

October 2007 — eight months until departure

For Christmas in 2006, Jared bought me my first briar tobacco pipe. It was a low-end Savinelli (of course I didn't—and still don't—know the difference between high- and low-end tobacco pipes). I was most enthralled by the idea of looking like a character in a Hemingway novel, or like Jay Gatsby or Sherlock Holmes. When I opened the dark blue box with gold lettering and folded back a deep purple cloth pouch to find the small, black beginner's pipe, the only thing I could say to Jared was: "You're the king of my vices!"

Of course, I was only joking. Jared, however, having only been my friend for three or four months, looked back at me concerned. "I guess I'll take that as a compliment?"

I nodded quickly and said, "Oh yeah, man, I'm going to be a total smoker now, and it's all thanks to you."

He didn't think that was very funny.

A year later I was facilitating a fall-semester discussion group comprised of primarily college-age guys. Jared's parents were kind enough to allow us to use their living room from seven to nine every Wednesday evening. The discussions we had were mostly based on the girls we liked and on our pastor's sermon from the Sunday before (usually in that order).

Around nine, when discussion seemed to lull, we would pray and close out the group. I always knew, however, when we had gone over because I would see a figure standing on the back patio lighting up his pipe. It was Eric.

Eric followed up with me often after our short trip to SLO, knowing how much our getaway and riding bikes had meant to me. We still worked together at the café, and sometimes when we'd close we'd drive up to a park to smoke pipes and talk about life. My favorite thing about Eric was how direct he always was. When he had questions for me, he was always concerned with how I was really doing. Often he'd look at me sideways and say, "Dude, come on—you can tell me how you really feel." He didn't care for times when I was trying to be sympathetic to people at the expense of myself, especially when it involved my ex. At this point in our lives, he believed that I had been wronged, and he was determined to do whatever it took to build me back up.

Eric knew we had our group meeting on Wednesdays and liked to show up right at nine to let us know that it was time to follow our spiritual conversations up with a great aromatic and a few IPAs. I'd try not to look through the window at him during prayer for fear of cracking a too-conspicuous laugh or smile. When the younger guys had left through the front door again, Jared and I would exit through the back to meet him. In this season of my life, this was often when the real spiritual conversations began.

One evening on Jared's darkened patio, where only the light from the living room helped to ascertain the silhouettes of our profiles and the glossy brown beer bottles we were lifting to our mouths, Jared decided to speak openly. He, Eric and I were just getting comfortable, each lighting our pipes and letting smoke flow effortlessly in and out of our mouths.

"So, it's the beginning of October," Jared said calmly. "And I can see you're already changing." Silky grey smoke poured from his nose and flowed through his beard.

I wanted to say that I believed him, or that at least I agreed, but nothing felt very different to me. I still rode around town alone listening to my music, and at that point had barely broken the surface with Alex. I still felt a long way off.

"I agree, man," Eric said quickly. "I mean come on, dude, look at you. Getting all slim and sexy. You're changing a lot. But the way you carry yourself. Something new is definitely happening." I knew Eric was right about trimming down, at least. Since I started commuting daily by bike three months prior, I'd dropped fifteen pounds.

"I wish I could say I felt the same way, guys," I said meekly.

"Dude, don't worry about that. You don't need to feel anything," Eric said.

"I know," I said. "I'm just ready to feel as new as you guys say I look."

We tamped, relit and took turns pulling in and pouring more smoke onto the patio.

"Dude," Jared said. "I've told you parts of my story about my ex-fiancée, but I don't think I've told you about my perspective."

"Okay," I said.

"I want you to hear me out, okay?" He was pointing his pipe at me.

"Sure," I said. I took a long drink from my beer and re-situated in my chair. I'd only really known Jared about a year, and compared to Tyler, Les and Eric, each of whom I'd known for at least three years, we'd already come a long way in our friendship.

"So I was in the same place your ex was in, and you were in the same place as my ex-fiancée."

I frowned, beginning to disagree and completely surprised that he would make such a connection. Jared was one of the classiest guys I knew. The idea of him doing anything close to what my ex had done was absurd.

He held up his hand. "Let me finish," he said, taking a puff of his pipe. "I knew the kind of love my ex needed, and I knew I was being selfish by keeping her around. But I still did. I kept her around for a long time, even though our love had been dwindling and dying for a long time. Soon, I just couldn't be the person that she needed."

The patio was quiet and I could hear cars passing on the freeway a half-mile away.

"It was one of the hardest things I've had to do—to walk away from somebody you're attached to but know you're not right for. But I knew it was the right thing to do."

This was difficult, and I wanted to tell Jared he didn't understand and that in his scenario he didn't have another love interest in mind, a best friend of hers to run off with. But I also didn't know that. On the other hand, hearing what he'd said made it hard to not sympathize with my ex. Maybe she knew it was right to let me go but just didn't know how to do it. Maybe formulating the words that Jared had just shared was just too hard for her.

Eric nodded and held up his beer. He knew where Jared was going with this.

"The point I'm trying to make is this," Jared said sitting up in his chair. I sat up too.

"Someday there will be a girl who'll come along and understand exactly what you need. If there's anything that keeps love more at a distance than not being understood, then I don't know what it is," he said, "except cheating. Or murder. Those might be worse." He leaned back and looked at his pipe, which had gone out. He took a drink and thought for a few seconds. "Find the girl who isn't afraid to peel back the layers. The one who yearns to understand you, to cheer for you, is the one you want to commit your life to."

"Damn right," Eric said, tipping his beer toward Jared for the cheers.

COMPOSITION

I don't know who it was growing up that taught me to journal my thoughts—more than likely it was a friend—but I do know I have always liked doing it. While at church I'd write notes on a pastor's sermon, often adding my own thoughts in the margins along with their points; after school when I was home from a shift at work and winding down for bed, I'd slide my journal from my backpack and pick up a pen. Back then, my journals looked like composition notebooks (the kind with the splotchy black on white sponge design). Through high school and into college I practiced writing all sorts of things. Poetry and short fiction were common, but more than anything I'd started to record my deepest thoughts, aspirations and fears. I remember being taught to always bring my concerns to God in prayer, and I always tried to try that first. From there, I'd continue by picking up my pen and letting my imagination take me into another world. My left hand anchored across the bottom of my pages, my pen poised like a blade in my right hand, I'd start pushing out letters and words, and after about four or five sentences, I'd be gone, raptured into a dream space, moving my hand and writing all the while but seeing only with my mind's eye.

Writing in my journal was, for me, a way to sort out life—pushing through the overgrowth of a jungle path and stopping to set up camp—to stop moving long enough to try to figure out where I was and who I was becoming. I believe God gave me journaling as a place I could go to be brutal in my honesty about all I was feeling and dealing with. And if God gave this to me—I reasoned—and if I'm able to be most honest here, where nobody else is listening or reading, then maybe God wants me to be really honest.

I eventually learned to know journaling as my best manner of prayer. I once heard that prayer is for rejoining in communion with God. Not that God ever left—rather, that I have left, do leave and will continue to leave God for the rest of my life. I think God gave me journaling so that I could more easily come back to commune with him, and maybe God gives everybody their own manner of prayer; I'm not sure, but I'd hope so.

KARAOKE & CIGARETTES

December 2007 — six months until departure

I would soon be co-leading a group of forty college students to New Orleans to help re-build houses. Coming off a last-minute team meeting at the church one night, several of us were too excited to go home and sleep before meeting back at the church again the next morning for our departure. So instead we darkened the already dimly lit double doors of a karaoke bar called Maverick's and quickly dropped our names and song choices into the queue.

I've never really liked karaoke. Mostly, it's because I don't know what to do with my body when a song goes to an interlude and I have nothing to sing. Having just sung my heart out for the first minute and thirty-five seconds and then seeing the dreaded "(Eight Bar Musical Interlude)," I nervously lower the microphone, close my eyes and pray to God that the song either accidentally ends early or that time speeds up. When neither happen, I sway a little, crack a nervous smile and try to dance, attempting to recreate some dance moves I used to see my friend Joe do in high school.

Just before midnight I noticed a few of my teammates stand and greet a couple that had just arrived. I began to turn my head but stopped halfway, knowing I didn't need to turn any farther. The knot in my stomach about singing my stupid song dissolved and morphed into anxiety. I tipped back the remains of my Newcastle just in time to hear my name called. I stood, pulled my hood over my head and walked to the stage.

A lurid four-hit crash, followed by a dreary electronic piano line, and I went straight into singing "Clint Eastwood" by the Gorillaz. I closed my eyes while I sang and before I knew it, I was halfway through. During the interlude I didn't sway or try to dance. In fact, I hardly moved at all. The only thing I did was stand there, bobbing my head, which was now full of thoughts that seemed to have percolated up from the feelings in my chest. I dreaded everything about leaving that stage. I saw them holding hands; I saw him glance at me once, and then twice; I saw how she never looked up.

I pushed through the convenience store door and realized I knew nothing about buying cigarettes. The clerk was a middle-aged Hispanic man and he was inattentive. I peered be-hind him at the palette of tobacco. Newports caught my eye because of their bright orange and sea-foam green packaging. I recognized Joe Camel from a commercial when I was a kid on the Camel packs. I saw six or seven different Marlboro cartons and remembered the cigarettes I smoked with Victor when we were twelve, one's he'd stolen from his brother's supply. We'd smoked them like criminals in an alley behind a Toys "R" Us. The taste was off-putting, but the feeling was exhilarating. I wanted that feeling again, or at least something like it—anything, really, to get my body to feel something else.

"Yes, amigo," the clerk said through a heavy hispanic accent.

I waved and stuttered, "Uhh, yes, uhh… Marlboro. Uhh… reds, please."

The man barely looked where he reached. "Five thirty-nine," he said.

I handed him a ten-dollar bill and tried to look cool, as if I bought cigarettes all the time.

He poured the change into my hand. "Four sixty-one," he said. "Need matches?"

I hadn't thought that far ahead. I just knew I'd be smoking. I nodded, still cool. He set three tear-and-strike packets into my hand. "Thank you, amigo," he said.

Outside, I peeled away the plastic wrapper and opened the carton. I pried away the foil and looked at the twenty perfectly aligned cigarettes. They were beautiful in their quiet, nestled order. I held the box in my hand with unintentionally motionless drama like I was contemplating the rest of my life. *So here I am,* I seemed to be thinking to myself. *A smoker. I guess that's how this is gonna go. I guess that's who I've been driven to be.*

When I attempted to pinch out the first cigarette I found it surprisingly difficult. I'd underestimated the efficiency of how tightly packed the box would be. Briefly, I thought about abandoning the idea altogether, wondering if it might be some kind of sign. I looked inside and could see the clerk staring distantly at a potato chip display with his arms folded. With my fingernails I eased the first cigarette up and out. I laid it between my lips and instantly tasted those rebellious cigarettes behind Toys "R" Us. I struck a match, lit the tip and pulled in a mouth of smoke. I forced myself to let it sit there, thinking it would be similar to smoking my briar pipe. As the smoke lingered I had memories of Disneyland in the early nineties when smoking was permitted, and I smelled the ashtrays from my childhood friend William's house. I pushed the smoke out of my mouth and wondered what the hell the fuss was about.

I took a few more drags before throwing it on the ground and breaking it apart under my foot. My mouth was coated now; I could taste the cigarette all over my teeth and tongue.

I peered at the night sky and could see there was no moon. There were several orange street lamps, though. I walked beneath them and then down the hill under the train overpass on Harbor Boulevard. With my hands in my pockets and my hood still over my head,

I tried to make smoke-like shapes with my invisible breath. I liked that better. It didn't taste as bad. I walked around town alone like this for close to an hour, knowing Jared or someone back at Maverick's might soon call to see where I'd gone. I knew Jared would understand why I left—though he might not have agreed with the cigarettes. I pulled the pack out of my pocket and studied it again.

I remembered something Eric said over the summer. He told me that someday I would be healthier and stronger because of my breakup experience. I didn't believe him at the time, and he said he understood why I didn't believe him. But then he'd said, "Honestly, man, you're really just better off without her. I know that's not fun to hear, but it's true." They were some of the hardest words I would force myself to hear. I attempted to hold them close for weeks after, like a soldier with a Bible at his breast, wanting to believe that I really was better off. It had been seven months now since the breakup, and while not fully healed, I had really come a long way. Counseling, friendships and a belief that prayer to Jesus even when those prayers felt entirely selfish, were not only getting me by but helping me get healthy again.

Marlboros in hand, I looked the pack over once more before setting it on a bench at a bus stop and walking back to Maverick's.

Everybody Loves America

The thin, blue sign is all Kansas offers as its way of introduction. They stop for a picture. Aaron tries to smile but can imagine the way he is gawking and starts laughing at the sight of himself in spandex with a goofy smile in front of a stupid little Kansas sign. From the other side of the road, Les stands in front a Colorado sign and frowns. This sign is larger, and with big green-and-white serif text it reads:

WELCOME TO COLORFUL COLORADO!

At a gas station, a man in plaid with boots and Levi's is walking from his Ford pickup and keeping his eyes on them. Just before opening the door he brings two fingers to his brow, saluting and smiling before walking inside. Another man in overalls and a dirty white T-shirt steps outside and glances at them, twice. The second time he looks more interested and stops walking in front of them and says, "Well alright, boys. Welcome to Kansas."

They wave.

"Temperatures peakin' at ninety-five today," the gas station attendant says to them inside. "Well, I'd say you oughta keep headin' down this road you're on, like you been doing since Colorado. When ya get to the town of Tribune you take a left and stop at the pool."

"The pool?" says Les.

"That's right. Most towns out here have a community pool. Dollar or two gets you in all day."

Les slowly closes his eyes and lets his head fall back. He smiles and mouths the word "yes."

"Thank you," Aaron says, waving and moving toward the door. They unlock and mount and push out on their bikes faster than ever. They barely glance left for traffic and never stop. They race.

Smaller towns in rural Colorado and Kansas have water towers. Most stand above everything else in town with big signs across the top displaying the city name and a slogan, such as: "Town of all towns," "The most colorful of all of Colorado," or "Land of superiority."

The town of Tribune has a water tower that, from far off, looks like an enormous grey golf tee. As they approach they pretend to look for God in the sky getting ready to swing. They joke that God probably doesn't play golf.

The orb-like tower of Tribune has no slogan, only "TRIBUNE" written four times around it, once for each direction.

The town is modest. There is an antique shop, a gas station, a library, chunky and broken concrete streets in need of repair and, of course, a pool.

"I wonder if Wendy Peppercorn will be on duty," Les says, alluding to a famous childhood movie scene in *The Sandlot* where one of the boys pretends to be drowning so that he can kiss the lifeguard, Wendy Peffercorn.

Aaron laughs and says, "Peffercorn."

"What?"

"Peffercorn, you mean."

"Whatever. I wonder if Wendy Peppercorns will dive in and save me so I can kiss her and we can go have nine kids together in the house I build for her."

"You've really got it planned out."

"Of course I do, man. Of course I do."

Admission to the pool is three dollars. There are kids everywhere, a disproportionate amount to the size of the town, and it is just like the *Sandlot* pool scene. Dozens of kids running, jumping. Mothers are teaching toddlers how to paddle with bright orange water wings. They are visibly disapproving of the other children running and jumping into the water.

There is a changing room, but Aaron and Les look down at their bike shorts and decide they don't care. Jerseys slung across their bikes, shoes and socks kicked beneath, they jump in.

"I could float here forever," Aaron says.

"How many more miles today?" Les says.

"Sixty, I think."

"That ain't bad."

"Five hours. It's only noon; the terrain is flat."

Les has his eyes closed and arms out. He floats and lets the water bob him gently up and down.

When they arrive in Scott City they find a grocery store. The clerk asks where they're headed and they tell him the story. He says he's never heard anything like it. He wants to know more but has customers in line who are less enthusiastic. In somewhat of a scramble to connect he says, "Well, did ya know you can camp in any park in Kansas?"

"Is that so?" Les says.

"Sure is. Go and check this one right down here." He points south. "Not but a mile away. You'll find a place there."

Just as promised, they find a park with plenty of space to spread out. Signs at the park's entrance are cautioning but condoning, reading: "Camp at your own risk."

The night arrives gradually in Scott City. They read books intermittently, chewing and swallowing their dinner while talking about the bike gang of Olney Springs, the pool, the Agia Sophia coffee shop in Colorado Springs and the Hendricksons—and how they miss the cool air of Colorado.

"Can't believe we haven't even been gone three weeks."

"We haven't?"

"Nope," says Aaron, looking at the calendar on his phone. "Day eighteen. That's what we just finished."

"We're not even halfway."

"Right."

"And we haven't even tried to jump a train yet?"

"Also right," Aaron laughs.

The night is now in full view. A longing for family and familiar faces comes with the darkness, pressing upon Aaron's chest. He thinks of Jared, Eric, his brothers and sister, friends at work and his parents, and he thinks of what riding his bike along nighttime summer streets in Orange County has always felt like. Having made it this far, he feels strong. Mostly though, he feels different. He feels an inexplicable newness inside, something he knows could only have happened on account of pushing himself beyond his comforts.

"Ah! We're not even halfway!" Les shouts into the air. The back of his head is on his pillow. He rises and holds his arms in the air. There is a house nearby shrouded by overgrowth. There is a playground without any wooden chips beneath the swings. There is tall grass everywhere. Les turns in a full circle. His eyes are wide. He soaks the night into his chest. "Tour life!" He yells.

The night responds with silence.

"Tour the United States of America!" He yells.

Moments later the town of Scott City actually does respond, as if cheering something back. Diamond-colored stars shoot into the air, and then, the black sky bursts into color. Red. Green. Red. Blue and red. Formations like hand-drawn stars, circles and little fly-like displays that buzz around in tiny circles before simmering out. Smoke lingering in the air.

They are on their backs, fireworks telling stories in the sky. When it is finished, Les says,

"I love Kansas." In the distance they now hear crickets, car engines and other indiscernible country sounds of Kansas.

"Happy Fourth of July," Aaron says.

"Happy Fourth, man."

July 5, 2008

Up, down. Up, down. Pull don't push. Faster not harder. There are indentations on the handlebars. Stop holding them so tightly. Spread your energy out! Give it to your legs, or to your heart, however that works. Give it to your will!

The wind is a force all across this part of Kansas. Depending on our direction, it either agrees with us, or attempts to bowl us over.

Miles of headwind. The short beard Aaron has begun growing is pulled with by wind against the direction he is traveling, and he can feel its resistance.

"Life is like this isn't it?" Aaron says aloud.

"That's right," says Les, almost smiling.

"Life is all about headwinds, hills and heat."

"Just like riding a bike."

"I never thought I'd hear that phrase used in that way."

"Life has headwinds, life has descents," Les begins to sing his song. *"Both are from the hands of the Looooord."* Again with the Johnny Cash baritone.

"That's right, man," Aaron says.

"What's that?" Les says, looking over.

"Life has descents too," Aaron says.

"Yes, yes, it does. And tailwinds, and caring people who tell you about pools, and wild flowers, and Wendy Peffercorns, and where in the hell was she anyway?"

They laugh.

"You know, I never considered the good stuff while we've been fighting this wind," Aaron says. "All I can think of most days, or all that's usually on my mind anyway, is finishing. Not being on my bike."

"And you're missing it," Les says, looking out at the fields, the open landscape. "All of this life passing in front of you."

"What life?" Aaron says sarcastically.

Les ignores him. "The beauty in all of this. It's all out there. No better way to live than by getting to take it in as we are, man. No better way."

There is a ladybug on Aaron's front quick-release lever, a component at the center of his front wheel that isn't more than a half-inch wide. The red speck doesn't move.

"Les," he says.

"What."

"There's a ladybug on my bike."

"Get a picture of it. Blog it. They'll love it."

Aaron aims and captures. He watches it for a time, glancing up at the road roving by in front of them.

"When did it have time to do this? To jump on? We haven't stopped in over an hour."

"Must be a fluke," Les says. "Or, wait. I don't believe in flukes, or luck either."

"What about chance encounters?" Aaron says.

"Same thing."

"Is it?"

Les nods, watching the ladybug. They are side by side, both peering down at it. They haven't seen another person in hours.

"Providence," Aaron says. "God's providence."

"Yes."

"So God made this bug leap into the air and land on my bike? As soon as I passed, it just jumped because of God?"

"I wouldn't say he made it do the jumping, but yeah."

"Compelled it to? Inspired it?"

"I don't really know how God interacts with bugs and nonhuman things. I've never thought to ask. But God does give humans the ability to choose things, and that at the same time God exercises his own will over the world."

"Compatibilism."

"Yes."

"Well, do we know what Compatibilists have to say about insects?"

"We? Well, I don't. Do you?"

Aaron laughs. "I haven't decided if I'm a Compatibilist."

The bug is about as lively as a stick for five miles until suddenly, she leaps and is gone. Displaced and set into a new community. She has made her own great American tour. Five miles for any insect might as well be coast to coast.

Rush Center is another small town. For dinner they cook rice, beans, diced apples and honey, and they call it tour-the-US jambalaya. Aptly so, as touring the country really is an experience in piecing life together, living out of two small bags, hoping there'll be water at the next stop.

"Something goes missing for us California boys," Les says. His stomach is full, his hands on his chest.

"What's that?"

"This." He points into the night, and at first there is nothing until a faint grouping of light sparkles into view. Fireflies. They flicker, and then burn out. Then, just as before, but ten feet farther, the group sparkles into view again.

They are finding the clock seems to move faster with each day. At first they'd had their schedule all under control—6:30 a.m. was wake-up time, followed by morning rituals of reading, silence, breakfast, packing, stretching and moving on. But this regimen didn't make it out of California. By the time they were camping in Arizona the clock seemed to have lurched forward. Seven o'clock became the norm. *No big deal,* they thought. *Thirty minutes was nothing in the grand scheme of things.* But to stay on schedule something had to go, which meant reading and practicing silence were finished. They told themselves they could read on their lunch breaks instead. Sleep was, of course, of the essence.

By Colorado they were rising around 7:45 a.m. *We gotta be better about this,* they said, and so they cut out stretching. But their bodies were sore and tired and all but begging for more rest. It coaxed, pulling on their minds, and prevailing. By the time they left Colorado Springs and were passing through Boone, Eads and Scott City, they were rising at 8:30 a.m., which meant breakfast and packing were a juggling act. *Stir the eggs and stuff your sleeping bag; take down the poles, fold the tent and pack a granola bar into your mouth.*

"What time is it?" Les says. He doesn't move. Aaron reaches for his phone tucked into the inner-woven tent pocket nearest him.

"Eight-forty."

"Agh."

Aaron yawns and stretches. "What kind of touring cyclists get up at nine and don't start really riding until almost ten?

Aaron pulls the tent flap back and stands up outside, surveying the grounds of the tiny, vacant park. Three large trees, a hedgerow they've set the tent in front of, a water faucet they used to wash pots and jerseys in the dark the night before and a giant mess of plastic and torn apart bread.

"What the—hey, uhh, Les?"

"Yeah."

"Where'd you put the bread last night?"

"Left it with the other food stuff. Why?"

"Well."

Les crawls out and stands. "Oh," he says. "Would you look at that. We've had a thief in the night. I'm getting the camera." He ducks in and quickly returns. "Coyote, or a fox I'd guess. Doesn't matter. We're gonna make a video. A mystery film, like a whodunit. We'll do it in one take and we'll post it online."

"Love it," Aaron laughs. "We can call it: Where da Bread Go?"

Les pans across the park and tells a nice story about how in Kansas nothing bad happens. When he gets to Aaron he gives an off-screen thumbs-up.

"Uhh, Les," Aaron can be heard saying. "Where da bread go?"

"What do you mean?" Les pans back around to his own face and says: "Why there's always enough bread in Kansas." He keeps the camera on his face while he holds a smile for a few seconds longer than necessary before returning to Aaron.

"Nope. Definitely gone. Definitely stolen."

He pans back to his face, recording himself chuckling in disbelief.

Pans back to Aaron, who is pointing at the ground. The camera follows and bits of torn plastic and hollowed out pieces of bread come in to view.

Les is still chuckling. "Well, hey now, what kind of prank is this? Well that's the... that's our... that's our bread!"

In the background Aaron says, "It got eaten."

"It got eaten," Les says in a whisper, *Blair Witch Project*-style. He pans across the grass again. "Eaten. All of it. Gone. Kansas. Kansas, why? Why?" His voice rises with each word.

"It was because we left it out," says Aaron in the background again.

"Why, Kansas, why?" He is yelling now. "Where da bread go, Kansas? Where?"

Les presses the shutter button again and the camera beeps off.

"Will it do?" Aaron says.

"It shall."

"Still don't have any bread."

Emerging from behind the hedgerow onto the road, bikes tied down and cleats clipped, they are hit by a funnel of wind.

"Ah. Well, then there's that again." Aaron says. The air is cool, though, and the sky a dull, grey blanket above. They pull windbreakers on and keep moving.

Two-lane highways. White lines on either side. Corn fields. No shoulder. Cars pass infrequently. They wave as if to say thanks, and depending on the driver, if they drive an old pickup with Kansas plates, the driver tends to wave back.

On occasion a semi-truck will pass from behind. They wave, the driver waves and the world keeps spinning onward. But from the other side, when a semi approaches at full force with the wind, they find they need to grip their handlebars for their lives.

"Dude."

"Yeah?"

"Semi."

"Yeah?"

"He's kinda in our lane."

"What?"

"Here comes. Hang on!"

The force of the wall of wind easily triples. Their bikes shake, their front wheels feeling the urge to take flight. Traveling at ten miles an hour before, they are reduced to around four until they can emerge from the vacuum that the semi pulls behind it. When it subsides, Les rides up to Aaron.

"That—" he yells, "—was awesome!"

"Like being in a funnel of air traveling at you going a hundred miles an hour."

"I thought we'd just stop moving at one point."

"The wind sucks, but the vacuum funnel is awesome."

"So true. I'm kind of looking forward to the next one."

"Me too."

The flat, unvarying fields of corn and grasslands in western Kansas have run their course. What once was a mystery, something only found in the *Wizard of Oz*, has now been discovered, covered and has grown old.

The horizon is far and flat. The Rockies are nowhere. Trucks appear in the distance ahead and vanish in the distance behind. *The world really is round.*

US 50 bends up slightly just before Hutchinson, which is where they plan to find their junction down toward Wichita two nights from now.

They pull off to ride a frontage road for a change. Homes are set up casually. If they have grass, it is overgrown. Bushes wrap around corners, enveloping and taking over rooftops.

Dogs bark and dart back and forth, chasing along their fences. There are few cars, many parked in dirt driveways. Rusted camper RVs are parked on lawns. There are mosquitoes everywhere.

A tiny sign reads:

WELCOME TO ABBYVILLE

"That's quaint," Les says. "I love how quaint that is."

They follow the two-lane road into town, coasting and feeling no wind from any direction. A girl with unkempt hair is sitting on her bike as they pass. "Hey, what's your name?" she calls. Her accent is heavy.

They turn and wave.

"Aaron," Aaron says. "And this is Les."

"Tour the US!" Les says, raising his arm.

They roll on.

When they reach the house at the end of the street, Les begins to slow. He looks across the lawn and down the side yard and stops. This house is easily the nicest and largest and the only one with grass that is somewhat under control. He dismounts from his bike and pulls an American flag from his bag, the kind that people fly from their car windows.

"Where'd you get that?"

"Cortez."

"Cortez?"

"Yeah."

"Just like, on the ground. Or did you buy it? Did you pay money for that?"

"I found it in a trashcan when we were walking out of the store."

"And you've had it the whole time?"

"Mmhmm." He peers at the front door and windows. A breeze catches the flag and it waves dully in his hand.

"So, what are you planning to do?" Aaron says.

"Well, everybody loves America, right? Especially midwesterners."

"Everybody loves America," Aaron laughs under his breath.

"I'm gonna see if we can stay on their lawn, or out back, or inside." He opens the gate and starts up the walk.

"When did we decide to start doing that?" Aaron says, but Les ignores him. A small dog yips and growls from inside the house, curtains dancing where it scurries beneath.

Les knocks and they both wait. Nothing. He knocks again. Still nothing. He leans toward the dog and waves the flag in front of its face. The dog is going ballistic. "Come on," he says, coming back down the walk. "None of these other houses even have grass but I think I saw a park a little way's back."

"Name's Montana Fry," the girl with the heavy accent says when they roll by her again. "What'd you say yours was again?"

They are unloading their bags onto a picnic table. A puppy walks around their stuff, sniffing it. They presume it belongs to Montana Fry. It lifts its leg and urinates on a picnic table leg, turning its head shamelessly at them midrelease.

"I'm Aaron," he says. "And this is Les."

"Mmmkaay," she says.

They continue unloading as little Montana Fry sits calmly at her bike as before. She has a small white shirt that's been stained with something beige, like oil. She wears pink shorts and no shoes.

"So what you plannin' to sleep out here too?"

"Planning on it. Yep." Les says.

"Well that's funny."

"We're just passing through. Just need a place for the night," he continues.

"I never hearda two boys lookin' like you do passing through this town to sleep in our park. That's funny."

"Do you have any brothers or sisters, Montana?" Les says. He has quit unloading, leaving dinner now to Aaron. He bats away a mosquito.

"Well, you bet I do, want me to go get 'em?"

"That's okay. What are their names?"

"Which ones?"

"Just your brother, or your sister. Do you have more than one each?"

"Well, I have my uncle and aunt living right there. Momma there. My sister that way. I live with Gramma and Granpa. That's where Remington and Reno live too."

"Who are they?"

"Remy is my brother and Reno's the baby."

Les looks at Aaron.

"Hey, so what you riding for anyway? Is it for the church?" Montana leans against her pink Huffy as if she has been talking to strangers passing through Abbyville for years. She can't be more than nine years old. She watches them indifferently, though her nose for the strange things they are doing is keen, and she leaves none of their actions unquestioned.

"Well, no," says Les. "Not exactly."

"Well, what exactly then?"

"We're riding to New York City."

"You're what?"

"New York. You ever been there, Montana?" Aaron says, now joining. He knows she probably hasn't. It was a stupid question.

"I ain't never heard of any boys like you going that far. Why would you do that?"

"Adventure," says Les.

"You're riding to New York for adventures? Where from?"

"California," Aaron says.

She stares at them. The puppy is romping around in the background, walking across their tent, which still hasn't been put up.

"What. This must be going years for you. When you start?"

"Almost three weeks," Les says.

The girl is silent. She has no reason to disbelieve them, though every reason to keep asking questions. She contains her inquiries for about a minute longer.

Les continues helping Aaron unload. Dinner is almost ready to start cooking.

"So, there's a man coming 'round here you should be careful of," Montana says, staring at their plastic bag of unopened pasta.

"Oh? What kind of man?" Les asks.

"Got a tank on his back. He's spraying things. I asked him what he was doing and he just looked at me and kept spraying. Then when he was done he said he had to spray at night, too, 'cause there's more bugs out."

"Insecticides," Aaron says.

"What?" she says.

"Oh, he's trying to contain how many insects live here."

"What's con-tain?"

"It's like manage. Keeping a good eye on something."

"Yeah, that's it. Momma says he just here to kill them skeeters you been swatting at. That's why I come over here to ask where you was going. You can sleep in our RV trailer if you want so you don't breathe in that inspectinsides."

Les looks at Aaron, who bats a mosquito from his arm.

"We're gonna get eaten alive out here, man," Aaron says.

"I know."

The girl is watching them. The evening has made its way in and a blue-and-white fluorescent glow appears above their heads when a lamp above the picnic table pops on above them. They see how many mosquitoes they're dealing with. They could fill an amphitheater with them. The entire town of Eads.

"Whose RV is it?" Aaron asks.

"Granpa's."

"Yeah," says Les. "Can you ask him?"

She has her feet on her pedals, arms steering and tires cutting through the grass like a mower on a rampage. She is gone in a flash.

The puppy sniffs their bags and then looks at them.

"Granpa" doesn't care to meet them. As they load their bikes into the RV, Montana's mother is walking over.

"Hope you boys don't mind."

"Oh no, how could we? This is great. Thank you," says Les, reaching outward.

She shakes his hand lightly. Her face is unmade and her hair has been pulled back for days.

"Come on, little girl. Let these boys sleep," she says to Montana.

Montana no longer has her bike. She watches them unload. Her questions have ceased.

"Thanks again," says Aaron, calling from inside and poking his head out.

"Don't worry about it. Ain't nobody using this. Just sits here. Daddy is planning to get rid of it anyway. He should too."

They nod and Les has a look of appreciation. It is completed by his arms, which are folded at his chest. He looks as if he has just inherited the RV.

Montana and her mother walk on.

"There are cornstalks ten feet in the air," Aaron says, pointing. They are pedaling toward Hutchinson, en route to Wichita. There is no wind. The air is light, the heat subdued.

"Incredible."

"I knew they grew tall, but not that tall."

"Wanna take a look around?"

"A look around?"

"Yeah."

"In the cornstalks?"

"Yeah. This is our trip and we can do whatever we want."

"Hmm."

"We don't even need to ride to New York, right? The journey is not about the destination."

"What's that from?"

"I don't remember."

"Okay."

"Okay?"

"Lets run through the cornfields."

"Yes!" Les says pulling back on his brakes and steering to the shoulder.

There are no excellent places to pull off. No turnarounds, and really no shoulder. White line, seven feet, yellow dotted line, seven feet, white line, fence, cornstalks. They can nearly touch the corn as they roll by. They lean against the fence and pull their bikes in as close as possible. It is a corridor of grey, green, yellow and sky blue. Shadows fall on them, if there are any at all. They are heading in the direction of the sun.

"Race you there."

"Race me where?" When Aaron turns he sees Les is already over the fence and running into the field, his footsteps crunching old stalk and drowning away into the rows.

Aaron peers in. The rows are fairly neat considering how large the stalks are and how many stand in the patch. There is a thick bed of fallen stalk branches that lie in a sort of haphazard way, possibly indicating that no farmer has been by to tend the stalks in at least a month or two. He folds back the stalks with his forearms and walks about ten rows in. When he looks back he can no longer see the road.

"Aaron." It is Les's voice.

"Yeah?" He yells into the overhanging mass.

"Cornstalks," Les calls, this time from a different place.

Aaron finds the camera in his pocket. He thinks of the movie *Signs* and he flicks the camera to its recording mode. He turns it toward himself. The camera dings on.

"I don't..." he says, looking around. "I don't know where I am. I thought I was touring but I teleported to this..." He pans the camera 180 degrees. As he does he catches Les's face peering out at him. His body is completely covered by a row. He is wearing blue, so he is hard to miss.

"We're in a corn patch... this ain't Kansas anymore, this is better... this is Cornsas!" Les yells.

Aaron shakes his head, letting out a guffaw as he repeats the word "Cornsas" to himself behind the camera.

Les hiccups and laughs. He regains: "There are myths about cornfields. I don't know them but I'm sure people have died in them."

Aaron is laughing now.

Les darts off and, like a dog, appears again fifteen feet away. "This is our tour!" he yells from further away.

"Look at that church," Les says.

"That's a church?"

"It's what the sign said back there."

"It's a giant boat. It's rounded at the bottom and sealed off like a boat."

Les studies it. "Yeah, so they probably made a replica of Noah's Ark. So what?"

Aaron stares at it. "I don't know, man."

"It's a church. It's meant to look artistic."

"That?" Aaron says, more indignant than he'd expected to sound. "That is art?"

"Yes."

"Come on, man. Look at how much money was wasted to put that thing together. So much money. You know how many kids starve because of decisions like these?"

Les is quiet. He is thinking, probably about what he wants to say, but he doesn't.

"I mean, come on, man," Aaron says. "Don't you think?"

"No," he says. "I don't. It's art. Not everything in the world needs to look like shit, or like another damn office building. Cathedrals were built as expressions of worship. People built their finest work so others would be brought to God. To me, totally worth it. Every time. Even if it's a poor replica of Noah's arc."

Now Aaron is quiet. They pedal. Signs for Wichita are appearing.

"I still think it was kind of cheesy looking," Aaron says, catching up and speaking more sympathetically.

"Well," Les says. "I don't."

"So, didja buy that bike off some rich guy or what?"

Aaron turns. Sun streams through the windows, into his eyes. Ray Charles is coming through the speakers above. There is a man staring at him.

"I'm sorry?" Aaron lifts an earbud that hasn't been playing any music.

"I said you musta got this from some rich son-va-bitch. She's a beauty. You've got a beautiful bike there," the man says. He points.

Aaron realizes he's pointing at his loaded down Surly. "Hey, thanks, man."

The man's clothes are large and his pants have a hole in the left knee. His red flannel droops over his body as if it is keeping him dry from an invisible rain. His face is unshaven but not bearded. His mouth a bowl of odds and ends: canines, cracks, chips, stains, holes. He smiles, stands and sits down across from Aaron, who is writing while Les has been stocking up at the grocery store. Aaron closes his laptop and lays his arms across his side of the table.

There is a peculiarity about the man. Now, he is talking about his government stipend. "Always never enough," he says over and over. "But, hey, anyway, where you from? Can't be here. Not with that accent."

"Accent? Yeah, we're from California. Southern California."

His eyes widen. "No shitting."

Aaron nods.

"Wow. Hey, Crystal," he peers back. He is holding a cane that comes to his waist.

A chubby woman in an armchair facing the other direction looks at him. Her face is sun beaten and shiny. "What's that?"

"These boys from Cali. So-Cal boys. They prob'ly from LA," he says turning back to smile at Aaron.

Crystal sits up straight and waves, smiling and blinking.

Aaron waves and wonders if Les might ask to stay with them. Then he wonders if they need anything. *Do they?* He looks them over again. *Is that presumptuous?* He thinks to himself.

"We've been trying to get out to your neighborhood."

"Oh yeah?"

"That's right. See, I'm a music guy. A musician. I'm just waitin' to be found out. Got my guitar over there." It is under the armchair he'd been sitting on earlier.

Crystal hasn't moved her eyes from Aaron, which he notices and then looks back at the man. "What kinda music?" Aaron says.

The man's eyes light up. "Rock. Mostly rock. I love Dylan though. Say," he says, holding his chin. "So you live in LA..."

"Well, I..."

"S'pose you could get me in. I bet the music scene out there is something else. Wichita, man. Wichita is where musicians go to die. Hey, could you find me a way in? Do you know the bands in LA?"

"The thing is..." Aaron starts to say. The man is literally on the edge of his seat. Sober, attentive. He is a dreamer, and LA, no matter how small and connected a city he's been led to believe it is, is his promised land. "Thing is, I really don't know the music scene."

"Oh," he says. "You don't?" He looks confused.

"Not really, no."

He sits up. "Kinda seemed like you would. Hey, you sure? I mean, it could be any old connection. This is my dream, you know. To be a rock star. To live on stage and to sing."

"I—I really wish I did, man. I'm sorry about that. I'm not even from LA proper, technically."

The man looks more understanding now, like he knew that asking Aaron was all he could do. "Hey, that's alright. Man, don't even sweat it."

Aaron smiles and introduces himself.

"Charlie," he says in return. "And my lady, Crystal, as you heard me say."

"Nice to meet you both."

"Say, what you doing out here in the middle of Kansas anyway?"

"Well, you saw my bike there, and—"

"A real beauty, I'm telling you, man. I'm telling you. So, what, you're taking a train? You got family out here?"

"Neither, actually. My friend—he'll be here soon—and I, we rode here. We're halfway to New York City."

Charlie stops swaying his cane. Baristas in the background call out drinks, and there is jazz still playing through the room.

"So, you rode that bike, that one right there. You rode it here?"

"Yeah."

"All-a-way to Kansas."

"That's right."

"And you ain't even done."

"Yeah, that's right," Aaron laughs.

"I ain't never heard of that in all my life. I can't believe it. Are you kidding with me, man? You pulled that bike all way here with your friend? I mean, people do that?"

"Some do, yeah. Crazy ones, I guess," Aaron says.

"No kidding," he says. "No kidding." He leans back. He starts laughing. "Hey, Crystal they's in more need than we are."

"What's that?" She says.

"Well, ain't you listening?" He looks over.

She shakes her head.

"They're going to New York, on those bikes."

"I ain't never heard of something like that," she says.

"That's what I told him. Hey, say," he says, turning back to Aaron. "Can we get you anything?"

The gesture catches Aaron off guard. "Oh, no—I mean," he fumbles his words. "We're good."

"Are you sure, brother? Kind guys like you deserve to smell good. Never know when the news will be following you and the interviewers gonna want to ask some questions. Can't be smelling bad for them, can ya?" He lightly nudges Aaron with his elbow.

"We can go to the Walmart," Crystal says, pointing out the window.

"No, no. Please, you don't have to do that. Really, we're fine, but thank you. Thank you."

"Not even a toothbrush? Hell, I can get a toothbrush for cheap, man. Ain't no setback for us. After all, you're the one living the dream. Not us. You're the one on the road and making it happen."

Now Aaron feels guilty, either because Charlie is giving and he couldn't be, or because he really is living the dream while Charlie is not.

"Nah, man. But, hey, you'll get there too. I mean, you'll make it happen. Your dream, I mean." Aaron is suddenly aware of what he is saying and how he is saying it. He can't know that Charlie from Wichita will ever actually make it to LA to become a musician. He can't know that he'll even make it out of Kansas.

"How'd you get there, man?" Charlie says.

"Get there? Umm," Aaron starts. "I suppose it was really just a leap. Like one giant leap into the unknown. My friend and I didn't know what we were doing. We just jumped and here we are. Halfway done."

"A leap. I like that. It's like you had no idea what could happen to you."

"I still have no idea, yeah. In many ways we just went riding and didn't stop."

"That's it. That's it right there," Charlie says, leaning back. "Man. Crystal, that's it. We just gotta go. We just gotta take the first jump."

"I mean, a little reason is required. But yeah."

"You on the web? Where can we find you?"

Aaron digs through his pannier and pulls two yellow cards into view. "It has our blog right there," he points.

"'Tour the US.' I like that. I do. S'pose I'll need to know how you made these cards here. Lady and I here are gonna be taking our own trip real soon." He stashes the card in his front pocket and stands. Crystal follows suit. They begin gathering their bags and layering them over their shoulders.

"Friend," Charlie says.

Aaron rises.

"Come on, man—are you sure?"

"Am I sure?"

"Sure you don't need the damned toothbrush?" he says, laughing and throwing an arm across Aaron's shoulder.

"No," Aaron says. "Thank you, but no."

They shake hands again and Aaron waves to Crystal. Soon, they are out on the sidewalk, stepping slowly. Charlie with his cane, swinging it in circles, and Crystal following close behind.

"I think I'm getting sick, man," Les says, returning to the coffee shop.

"How so?"

"My head. Stuffy nose. I can feel it. Sore throat will be soon to follow," Les says, pointing at his throat.

"What do you think?"

Les looks on, his pupils wide, his thoughts somewhere in his eyes.

"I think I shouldn't ride. I need another night's sleep."

"Might put us behind."

"It will put us behind."

"I bet there's another option."

"There has to be. There always is."

Aaron is ripping a receipt into small squares. The highway running through the city is less than clamorous even though it is rush hour. Street lamps pour orange from their heads, but the sun is long from setting.

"Let's try to hitch another ride."

Aaron is quiet and he lets out a sigh. "Another?"

"Why not? I stand by the philosophy."

"The philosophy that we don't actually have to ride."

"That's right."

Aaron tosses the receipt squares into the air.

"How about this," Les says. "We ride a few miles up, out of town and out of sight, and try to hitchhike for an hour."

"And if it doesn't work, then what?"

"Stay in Wichita another night. Camp somewhere. I don't know. It's hitchhike or take a bus, man. I shouldn't ride."

Aaron jingles some change in his pockets. "Alright. Let's just give it shot."

"Okay."

East of Wichita, where residential blocks give way to farming plots again, there is a major junction, the north-south route coming up and over the east-west route and pouring away into the distance in both directions.

They wait atop the exit ramp where the highway heads east. Aaron finds a red ink marker on the shoulder and an old beer box. He tears away one side and turns it over, studying the blank side.

"What do you think?" Les says, looking at the cardboard.

"Probably the same way we wrote the one for Mexican Hat back in Utah. Man, remember that? Feels like forever ago."

"Yeah man, definitely. And good call," Les says wearily.

The marker has not dried out yet. It flows finely as Aaron draws letters:

EASTBOUND

GOT ROOM?

Les stands ahead about a hundred feet with his thumb out. His body droops slightly and he shifts his weight frequently. He holds his head when no cars are coming.

Aaron holds the sign for every car that passes, but hoists it especially high for trucks. With Les down, it is up to him.

After thirty minutes, Les is sitting on the curb with his elbow rested on his knee and his thumb lying to the side. His face is planted between his knees. When he doesn't move for a few minutes, Aaron puts away the sign, walks back to him. "Alright, man," he says consolingly. "Let's go back."

Les nods and stands.

With their bikes under their bodies again they look down the highway ramp once more. No headlights. Nothing leaving Wichita tonight.

"Greyhound?" Les says dimly.

"Sounds good."

There are signs leading back into the city. The first time they've ridden west in a long time. They follow cars, brake lights. They pass chain restaurants and grocery stores with empty lots. They ride by a dark schoolyard on the right and a DMV on the left. *Nobody walks this side of Wichita. Nobody rides a bike here either.*

A sign points south for the Greyhound station. Aaron leads and wonders if they'll even find a bus heading east at this hour. Les lets his head droop while coasting behind.

The station is lit with two fluorescent parking-lot lights, and underneath the bus loading dock there are several more. There are mosquitoes, there are oil stains, there is old gum everywhere. Signs of people who have boarded here in the past, but tonight the lot is empty. There are no buses in sight.

Les leans his bike against a brick wall and lies across a concrete bench. He wraps his arm around his face, his free arm dangling toward the sidewalk.

The doors to the waiting area locked and the blinds are shut. The hours read: 4 a.m.–10 p.m. Aaron finds his phone in his bag. It reads: 10:15 p.m. This means they've likely just missed not only a bus, but also a chance to sleep inside.

"We have to wait until four."

"Okay. That's fine."

"You sure? I mean, I don't see much else around. We might just as well stay."

"Yeah. I can't move anymore anyway."

"Okay, man. Rest up. I'll figure it all out."

"Thank you." Les is pale, especially under the fluorescent lights. His body completely relaxed.

Aaron wraps the bikes together with the cable lock and snaps it together. He pulls out a book and his note pad and sits against the wall near the bikes. He opens the book and watches the night. Nothing in Wichita looks alive. Nothing, but himself.

A voice. It is close. Very close. Aaron sits up and there is a short man peering down at him in jeans and a ripped T-shirt. He has neither teeth nor shoes. The way he sways his arms back and forth makes him look as if he is in a musical. He speaks as if he's running from something.

"I'm sorry—what did you say?" Aaron says.

"Says it's a late night for youse to be out here—out here in the station—catchin' sleep is all I see. All I see is two guys catchin' sleep." He laughs playfully.

"Tryin' to catch a bus is all," Aaron says, looking across the lot. Still nothing. He rubs his eyes.

"Oh yeah—I done caught a bus out here 'bout six months ago—travel to Alabama see my momma. She tol' me, come on down—says to her I ain't got no money, Momma!—well what you think of that? And she says fine, okay. That's just fine. Go get you some money from the Western Union cuz I sent some."

"Oh yeah? That's real nice of her."

"Real nice, real nice, that's right—that's the only way to live, that's what she always say to me—be nice to people and people be nice to you. Hey say there, boy, I know youse sleepin' and all out here in the hood, but say, you got any change? Maybe a dollar or some quarters?"

Aaron feels his pockets for his wallet, then his phone. "Yeah, I might have something." He stands, realizing how much taller he is than the man.

"Hey say now. Dig deep, real deep—take a big ol' scoop!" The man sways his arms again, smiling.

Aaron scoops and pulls up eighty-seven cents. He hands it to the man and watches him count it. Vodka breath, mouthing the worth of each coin: "Fifty, seventy-five, eighty, eighty-five 'n cents to spare from a nice man like yourself. Hey, man," he says. "I hope for your sake my momma was right."

"Thanks," Aaron says. "I do too."

"Hey, you got any more in them pockets? Come on now, I gots ears—I can hear change ever' time it makes a sound."

"Sorry, man. Nothing left."

"That's alright, that's alright—hey say, my name is Benjamin, and you have yourselves a nice sleep there—catch a nice bus to wherever it is youse goin'—but make sure they don't take you back here again. Ha ha ha! Alright then. Goodnight then. Goodnight."

Aaron waves and tucks his hands in his pockets. Benjamin moves quick, swinging his arms, and turns a corner.

"Big ol' scoop," Les says from the bench.

"You heard that?"

He nods.

"So much energy in him. Such a smile across his face too, like he loves life. Like he, yeah... Like he loves his life."

Les says nothing.

People begin arriving at 3:30 a.m. A city bus lets a dozen people out and they roll their bags under the overhang and lean against the wall. Some light cigarettes and read newspapers. Children rest on their parents' laps. The sun is still hours from rising.

Aaron nods in and out of sleep until a young woman emerges from a small Honda Civic, dressed in navy slacks and a sky-blue blouse. She wears a small, white name tag and carries keys. She slides a key into the door, pushes it open and ducks inside.

People rise unenthusiastically and Aaron follows them inside. The waiting area surrounding the ticket window could be a poorly ventilated hospital waiting room. There are blue-padded chairs and magazine racks. There is a Pepsi machine and a grey drinking fountain.

The television screen above the ticket window flicks on. There is one bus to Dallas and another to St. Louis, the latter of which would leave in an hour. Aaron does the math, figuring St. Louis to be four hundred miles away, and not only able to catch them up but sufficient to propel them two to three days ahead of schedule.

He stares at the television screen. *Something else might come up. Springfield, Missouri, would be nice. It would feel less dishonest that way. Two hundred miles instead of four hundred. Two hundred miles less that I'd have to admit I didn't ride when I get home.* He considers Les's current state, though, and decides it will have to be St. Louis. He pays for two tickets and thinks about getting to enjoy the tour more because they'll be ahead of schedule.

Kansas becomes a dream. Nowhere and nothing to see at 4:30 a.m. Aaron remembers day three, leaving Indio around the same time. California has felt like a memory for a while. Nearly fourteen hundred miles ago they were just beginning. Dreams still fresh on their hearts.

The bus sways like a boat. Wide turns, long, slow acceleration; clunking gears, back and forth. The engine roars and burns; it quiets as the clutch is shoved to the floor, the sound of gears cutting through grease and oil, the engine roaring again.

Miles are swallowed like one large gulp of water. Refreshing, but shocking to a system so used to sipping miles every six to ten minutes. On a bike, the world is a different color. It is the color of dirt, rocks, crevices, trees, the veins of leaves. But on the same roads in an automobile, it is just blue, brown and green.

All aboard the bus sleep save for the wrinkly driver with his ampm coffee behind his translucent door. At a rest stop in Kansas City he throws his door open, stands, holding the buckle of his belt and yells: "We leave again in four minutes." With that, he is down the steps and into the restroom ahead of his passengers. Most remain asleep. Most don't even know the bus has stopped.

A gentle hum of the idling engine, and in what seems like thirty seconds there is a roar, gears clunking again, another roar, and they are turning back onto the highway.

The bus is a night-borne vessel, calmly making its voyage across the land. There is stillness outside, a silhouetted tree line, dew rising. The sun slugs upward, a slit of glow above the Ozarks and valleys of greenery. In minutes they are coming to life. It is the first time in almost a week that the earth around them has not felt brown and dead.

I THINK I LOVE YOU

When I was nineteen, six months was how long it took.

When I was the boyfriend of Brianna and then Tamara back in junior high, it took three weeks. I'd let it drop from my loose tongue often as a child suddenly interested in something on television. Back then, I didn't understand how it worked or what it meant. I just knew it meant something and that I wanted to say it.

When I got older I started to stall on it, as if I believed that words had power. I decided that being quick to give it away seemed haphazard, as if some floodgates would suddenly open and I wouldn't be able to control how hard and fast it would all hit me. I saw myself getting pummeled by emotions I couldn't control. So, I told myself I'd save up the phrase *I love you* when I got into future relationships and share it only when I believed I knew something undeniably true about my feelings for a girl.

Sometime around the six-month marker, I was taking my first writing class at Fullerton Community College. It was Introduction to Creative Writing, and aside from reading a few articles, our only assignment all semester was to write a story somewhere between ten and fifteen pages. This was the first time I'd ever been asked to write creatively, and it was a challenge. I found I was hopelessly bad at it, and I procrastinated greatly. My teacher's few requirements for the story were that we needed to establish a setting, identify main characters and then show how at least one of them changes (becoming better or worse) on account of some event happening to them.

I got really into making my characters do things and go places, saying funny things and wasting time and trying to have fun all around. Mostly, they preferred to hang out. It was, unbeknownst to me at the time, a fictitious story about my high school friends and me. The title was "Wish You Were Here," and this was something I came up with well before I ever started writing the story, probably because I was listening to a lot of Pink Floyd. I decided it would be a call-out to something that would happen at the end of the story, and more than likely this would mean one of the friends would have to tragically die.

When I turned the story in, it was rather mediocre. Plus, it didn't have an ending. Somehow I couldn't get myself to close it off, and instead it simply carried on for ten or eleven pages with little ever happening. I didn't know it at the time, but later I realized I'd been afraid to hurt my characters; I feared imposing upon them because I thought they might become people I couldn't control, and so I let them keep doing whatever tame things they'd do, and never getting them to the point of needing to grapple with anything character altering.

But six months. She and I were driving through downtown Fullerton in my Volkswagen Bug with the heater on high. This inevitably fogged my windows, so I always carried a squeegee in my side door. Pulling up to a red light I'd slick away the condensation and peer out at the blurry streaks of red coming from the traffic signal until I'd see that it had changed to green. I'd slick the windshield every minute or two, even while driving, pretending all the while that I could see the road just fine.

The Bug was loud. Fired up in first gear until fifteen miles per hour, I'd yank down the stick, and the engine would slide into second; another climb up to twenty-five miles per hour, and I'd slide it into third; then fourth at forty miles per hour where things felt just right.

She in her glasses, her brown curls falling over her light winter coat, would glance over and smile at me as we drove. It was our sixth month anniversary and we were coming from dinner and were headed to my place at the El Dorado Apartments on Placentia Avenue to watch a movie when suddenly I got the idea. It was only sudden, though, in the sense that I'd decided I wanted to carry out the idea tonight, right now even, and not that I'd only just realized I wanted to do it. I'd been waiting to do it for months, to be honest. Even more, I'd been waiting to tell a girl for years, wanting desperately to cover up my careless junior high babblery.

I popped the Bug into neutral and coasted through the light at Madison and pulled up to the curb in front of my apartment complex. I left the engine running, kept the heater on, my left hand still on the wheel and my right atop the stick. I looked over. She looked too. I was remembering everything I could about being in junior high and saying all the stupid things I'd thought would garner me affection and love. The difference was that with her I felt I knew. This, I was sure, was because I was enraptured, feeling purpose in being with her, knowing I was meant for big things like missionary work in Darfur precisely because she'd told me how great she thought I'd be at it. I'd had visions of her and me moving somewhere destitute and remote, helping people however we could. I had grand ideas of what being a husband—her husband—could be like, regardless of what anyone said or may have been trying to hint to the contrary.

I placed my hand in hers and continued to look across, the Bug's engine still running, humming, the heater hotter than ever. I wanted to be able to say exactly what I knew to be true, but if I was honest, I didn't actually know. I just felt.

"I think," I started. Three cars quickly rolled by on my left and the Bug slightly swayed from side to side. I regained the moment. "I think I love you," I said.

She smiled. "I know. I think I love you too."

Part IV.

Land of Hospitality

The air is dense for the first time all trip. From the Greyhound station, they pedal across the city of St. Louis and up Fourteenth street, wearing the blanket of humidity coming off the Mississippi. There is no wind, just thick air. People in cars with their windows up. It is ten in the morning and traffic is light.

They stop at a McDonald's for food and to consult a map online. There has always been a vague plan to make it across the country by going mostly east and slightly north, specific roads, trails and highways being somewhat unimportant. Manhattan is, of course, latitudinally farther from the equator than Los Angeles. The quickest way to go would be in a straight, diagonal line. Drop the pin in the west and pull the second one across with a string and plant it somewhere just off the Hudson River, and you've got the quickest way from point A to point B. Fortunately (or unfortunately, depending on where you've got to be), the eastbound road to New York City is anything but straight. At this point, in St. Louis, they need only to travel the vertical distance of West Virginia before they'd be as north as they'd need to be all trip. East-west would still need at least another week and a half.

They calculate the number of miles remaining on Google Maps and come up with nearly 1,200.

"That's only a third of the entire trip to go," says Les, doing quick division. "Aaron, can you believe that? We are already two-thirds there."

They are quiet, chewing hamburgers and recalling the entire year of planning they'd done, realizing they were well over halfway.

"We're almost finished," Aaron says solemnly.

"Remember riding our first century?"

Aaron laughs. "Yeah. OC to San Diego. That hundred miles sucked."

"Hot as hell then, just like today. And now look at us. We're carrying all we need in the world with us on our backs, and we've ridden more than halfway across America already."

"Kinda makes you feel like we should keep going."

Les looks up blankly. "Man. There's only a couple things in my life keeping me from making that a reality."

"Family?"

"More than that. I am hesitant to even say it, but it's just a job after all. Then again, maybe I'd change my mind in ten years. Maybe when I'm thirty-three I'll want to settle down—whatever that means. Maybe my wife and kids will need me to do that. At that point the adventure is definitely a different one, but no less exciting."

"So, it's your job that keeps you from continuing on?"

"I'm going to be a resident coordinator at my old school."

"Yeah, man," Aaron says. "Suits you well."

"Thanks," Les says quickly.

"So, if you weren't going back for that job, and if instead you were going back to something more mediocre—"

"I'd never do that," Les says.

"What?"

"Something mediocre."

"Oh."

"Would you?"

"I guess I hope I wouldn't."

"No man, of course you wouldn't. You decided to ride a bike across the country. Of course you wouldn't do something mediocre. And neither will I."

"So."

"So, if I were coming home to no job at all, or to no family, or to no girlfriend, then yes. I would absolutely keep going. This is a trip of a lifetime, but the job is something I've always wanted to do, too. This summer I get to have both."

"A trip of a lifetime and a dream job."

"Yep. Exactly."

"That's pretty cool, man."

From the Poplar Street Bridge they have to act fast. US Route 41 and Interstates 55 and 64 all merge and form one line above and over the Mississippi River. It is a highway that connects Missouri to Illinois. They crank, knowing they shouldn't be on this bridge at all but also knowing any other bridge would take them miles out of the way. The sway and weight of their luggage is second nature, and their lungs have become like compartments made of iron. They pull across the bridge and look back from a turn-off. The skyline is grey, red and white concrete. Along the waterfront stands the nation's tallest man-made structure. Six-hundred-plus feet into the air is the famous Gateway Arch. Aaron remembers aerial shots of it from when the Dodgers would play away games against the Cardinals.

Every stretch of road, every turn, every field of green we pass is an accomplishment. It's a dream, really. I used to think that getting to a destination was the only thing that mattered, and that to say I finished was the greatest accomplishment. But Les and I have been on the road a long time now, and we've covered a ton of ground. I'd say that's one of my greatest accomplishments—just getting this far. It was way farther than I ever thought possible, and that's something I'm proud of. That's plenty.

They coast along Missouri Route 15 until splitting off east along Route 177. The air is a damp sweater in their throats now, heavy with moisture. As dense as it is, they are glad for it. It seems to land on their exposed arms like dew that cools their bodies. As they ride, they enjoy the refreshment it brings, but when they stop momentarily, they sweat tropical storms. It is far better than ever to keep riding.

City structures and billboards last for fifteen miles, but soon they are in the country again. Forty-five miles east of the city is a tiny town called Okawville. In Okawville, there is American spirit. Flags hang from every street lamp; dark green grass pokes neatly from the earth; and quaint, finely-painted homes pattern each block. They stop for a cold drink at a convenience store that sells an absurd amount of ice cream and decide a cone sounds nice as well. When they return to their bikes, Aaron has a flat.

Les stands above. He licks his ice cream and looks at the sky, his blue jersey catching in a breeze. "Ah well," he exhales. "That sucks."

"It does," Aaron says, standing closer. He sips his melting cone. "Man, I—" he trails off.

"Yeah?"

Aaron looks down the road and back at Les. "Want to just call it a day? I'll deal with the flat in the morning."

"That's an idea," Les says, looking around. "There's plenty of yards out here. Plenty of places to throw out a sleeping bag."

"How about that one?" Aaron says, pointing across the street. It is a modest home, surrounded on all sides by tall grass. It stands on a corner and there is a man outside, without his shirt on, watering the bushes along the windows.

Les is already halfway across the street, ice cream dripping down his hand. Aaron can see them conversing and the way the man shrugs and points toward his backyard. When Les returns he is composed, licking his cone. "Yep," he says, picking up his bike and wheeling it back toward the house. "Camp time."

"So," Aaron starts, while throwing the tent across the back lawn. Les is opening a can of beans. "Been thinking more again about what you've said about this trip not being about the destination."

Les stops unscrewing the lid but his hands remain around the small can. The can opener dangles in the air.

"It's just. It's weird. For all my life I've thought of life as something I haven't reached yet. Like something that's out there and that if I just keep putting my head down, one day I'll find it."

Les nods, his eyes fixed.

"I've realized that there's a lot that gets missed when you do that, you know? There are flowers you forget to smell and people you're supposedly too busy to talk to."

"Friends you ignore, family you dread talking to," Les says matter-of-factly.

"Exactly. I guess I'm realizing how dull life can be if we only have the end in mind. If we only live that way then we wind up missing a ton of really great things about life."

"This world is beautiful, like I've been saying. It'd be a shame to miss it."

"That's exactly what I mean. It'd be a shame to miss how incredible life is. The Rockies, or how exciting it is to feel the wind on your face as you dodge oncoming semitrucks."

Les peers at the purple sky. The street is lit by porch light. Cars are parked, and a breeze moves along the east-west route.

Eighty miles outside of Okawville is a small farming town called Albion. They arrive around five in the afternoon and begin knocking on doors for a place to stay.

Les does most of the talking, picking up his American flag and walking up the steps of a couple different porches. Aaron stands by the bikes and peers down the road. There is a house about every four hundred yards. At this one there is no answer.

They try the next one. Still, no answer. At the fourth house, the property begins with a barn right along the road. There are two large pickup trucks and an ATV quad with pieces of hay stuck to the tires.

"Number four," says Les energetically.

"This is a bad streak."

"True."

"We might be better off just sleeping in a field. Half these people aren't even home. They'll never know."

"Also true."

"I'm beginning to wonder if this actually works," Aaron begins to say just as a man in his sixties emerges from the barn. He looks at them, noting their presence, and keeps walking.

Aaron looks at Les and rolls his eyes.

"Excuse me, sir," says Les.

The man turns. He wears overalls and a red plaid work shirt. His boots carry mud. "Yeah? What is it?"

"My name is Les, and this is Aaron." Les places his palm across his chest. "And we are riding to New York from California. We're about done riding for the day and are wondering if there might be a chance we could camp on your lawn or on your property somewhere."

The man looks at them each once and then at their bikes.

Aaron feels his no coming as a wave waiting to break. Embarrassment rising and the desire to keep moving building, he wonders why they even try, and why this man would even consider saying yes.

"My lawn?"

"Yes, sir," Les says.

"You need to camp?"

"Yes."

"Well," the man says. "My name is Greg, and you've come to the right place." As he begins to turn, raising his arm to point, he says. "And boy do I have a place for you."

Now Les looks at Aaron.

"Come along now," Greg says, throwing a leg over his quad. "Follow me to the forest."

"The forest," Aaron whispers to Les.

"The forest!" Les says.

Greg rolls ahead and they quickly mount their bikes. They ride in a line: Greg, Les and Aaron. They pass Greg's house on the right, a tool shed with a large tree hanging over it on the left. There is a pen with sheep, a stable with horses. Greg leads them out across a field and opens up his throttle and roars over two small hills that are surrounded by corn on either side.

They laugh and crank to keep up. They roll over hay and cornstalk, rocks and dirt. They crest the first hill and fly down the other side.

Greg is waiting at the top of the second hill. "You alright?" He says as they meet him again. "Said you been riding from California, right? Thought you'd be keeping up!" he says, laughing and throwing his throttle back, burning toward a row of tall trees.

When they arrive, Greg points out a lake, a fire pit and the best places to set up a tent.

"Greg," Aaron says. "What is this? I mean, did you have this grove put in? Or this lake?"

"Oh, minimal constructing. Mostly just fixed everything up so that my family would have something nice to enjoy."

"This is every hiker and touring cyclist's dream," says Les.

Greg nods with his hands on his hips, proud of his backcountry oasis. "We're a giving family," he says. "That's what we do. Things are meant to be shared. I guess if there's a lesson to all this, it's that. So don't forget it."

They nod and look across the lake.

"Well, I got work to finish. You all get settled in." His quad engine roars at the turn of his key. "Oh and, guys, dinner's at six thirty. We'll see you then." Greg pulls his throttle back and races away, disappearing down the first slope, and flying over the second.

"Nobody is going to believe this," Aaron says.

"This is amazing."

"Right, incredible, but I never, ever, thought this kind of place existed on anyone's farm, let alone that we'd get to use it."

"People want to help people," Les says as he walks toward the deck leading into the water.

Aaron looks over the river and then behind his shoulder toward the house.

At dinner they meet the rest of the family, including Greg's wife, their daughter and her husband and Greg's grandson. The small dining room is filled with a home-cooked meal of potatoes, greens and roast beef, paired with conversations about road stories and small-town living. Afterward, when all the pie and ice cream they can fit into their bellies has since been put away, Aaron and Les ask if they can get a picture with the family. Greg's wife says something about not wearing enough makeup and Greg throws his arm around her.

Aaron sets the timer and runs to the side of the group, and someone pulls him in close. He looks across the faces of smiling people. *This is how it is supposed to feel. This is family. This is hospitality. This is sharing, community and love for your neighbors.* He glances back at the camera just before it sends a great white flash into the night.

THE PURPOSE OF THERAPY
(PART ONE)

February 2008 — four months until departure

Though the air-conditioning was on in the small counseling room Alex and I had met in over the past five months, I still fanned my face with a piece of paper. I'd ridden my bike from Brea to the counseling center in Fullerton, up and over the hill on State College Boulevard, where at the top the sky is big and on clear days you can see Catalina Island, downtown Los Angeles and Mount Baldy. I zipped quickly down the backside of the hill, my cyclometer reading thirty-five miles per hour, then thirty-eight, then forty, forty-two, forty-four, forty-five, until I stopped noticing my speed because my arms started to shake from gripping my handlebars so hard. I pulled the brakes and carved through a few residential streets until turning left onto Nutwood and pulling up to the counseling center.

"So, are you getting excited about riding?" Alex had just entered the room. He was five minutes late but he looked casual. I didn't mind. I liked having a few minutes to gather my thoughts.

"About the bike ride, or about Les getting himself and me in shape? Because honestly, I'm a little freaked out about the training regimen he's been putting us through."

Alex laughed. "Let's start with the bike ride. Do things like long journeys bring you joy or a sense of life?"

I thought for a moment. "I guess I want them to. I mean, I want to feel alive on account of this one, yeah."

He was quiet and looked attentive.

I continued. "But I love that Les is getting to have this trip, too. He's getting to dream big because of it. As a sidenote, I think that if there's anything I could ever wish to help people do, it would be to help them dream big."

Alex frowned as if he was thinking. "But the trip was your idea. It was Les that made it happen, right?"

"Yeah," I said. "Definitely my idea."

He held his notepad steady. "May I make an observation? Something that is entirely reflective of what you've been sharing over the past several months?"

"Sure," I said. Observations were great, but I wouldn't have minded a little advice here and there, even though I knew Alex wouldn't give me any. In one session he'd made it a point to tell me he would never lend advice. I figured Alex and all therapists must have signed some "therapy code" promising to never give advice.

He quickly skimmed his notes. "A little while back you said you don't deserve to feel as good as riding the bike makes you feel, and that you don't deserve to be this able to love your life. And just now, after I asked you if long journeys bring you life, I think I heard you deflect answering much about yourself and instead saying that you love helping people make their dreams happen. That's not bad, and in fact it's good. But I'm hearing some mixed things. Do you see what I'm saying?"

I did, and I slouched in my chair. There was a peculiar tingle in my chest, one that made me feel a little vulnerable. I've always liked coming across as the guy who could joke around but had it all together, and I wanted to keep it that way. Still, I suffer from a condition that I liked to call I'm-Really-Not-That-Bad Syndrome. Symptoms of my condition were denial that anything was ever really that wrong with me, suppression of any facts seeming to indicate that there might really be something wrong with me and secret lashings of anger between my fists and my Volkswagen Bug's plastic steering wheel when, in fact, I learned there was something wrong. Alex hit something deep, and the sky of therapy was starting to open. I was learning what therapy was for.

"Do you want to talk about it?" he said.

I waited to see if the tingling would go away. I wanted to say yes because I was at therapy and the point of therapy was to talk through the hard stuff with somebody. But I kept hearing myself rationalize. No, no. I'm fine. I don't actually need this.

Mostly, though, I was scared of admitting something I'd realized. In the months that followed the breakup, I became the center of many of my friends' concern, which was great at first, but soon felt as if I was receiving too much attention, either because I didn't want all of it, or because I didn't like that I wanted their pity.

I did need all the love and affirmation that I could get, though. But sulking by myself came easier. When out on my bike alone and listening to music, or while journaling in my room, I could sit in my own little fire, letting the flames around me flare up and dwindle whenever they would. Just as I'd been piling up complaints like paper straw wrappings in front of Les and Jared at the coffee shop, I liked being able to control something. But I was also scared because therapy with Alex was challenging that control.

After a moment I looked at Alex. "Well, I guess I've wanted to get away on the trip because I was heartbroken."

Alex wrote that down.

"And, like I've said before, she and I dated for a long time."

He looked up and nodded.

"Almost three years, and—well, we just did everything together. I'd be lying if I didn't say that who I was got wrapped up in her determination of me. I knew who I was because I was with her. Does that make any sense?"

He nodded again. "What I hear is that you found some identity in this girl, right?"

"Yes, exactly. Identity. It was like she let me know who I was. But it all sounds really stupid now. It's been several months and I don't even know if I should be that bothered by it anymore."

"Well," he said, "I wonder if at this point you still want to get away on that bike trip as you've said before."

"Yes," I said quickly, "I really do."

"Care to tell me about that? Does it have to do with her?"

"Partly does, yeah. And I have this friend, Drew, who told me that a trip like this will take me more places than I could know I need to go. I don't really know all he means by that, but at the end of the day I do still want to get out of here. And again, yes, I think it's partly because of her."

"So you want to get away, and you think that is partly because of this girl and how much identity you found in her."

"Yeah, I think so."

"Okay, good. Good. So, before we talk about being out on the road, is there anything more about this girl that you'd like to talk about?"

I sat still for a while and let my mind wander. Soon I began to get uncomfortable. I told that to Alex, and he asked if I wanted to keep going. I said I did, and as I sat back I could see that something was forming in my mind. Two clouds were coming together that I knew, once fused into one, would begin pouring rain. Before long I knew what I had to tell Alex, even if it was difficult.

"To be honest, what hurt the most was that the guy she chose to run off with was my best friend." As I said this I felt overwhelmed with shame, as if I was admitting their guilt, as if I was giving up their coordinates and exposing them by mentioning their actions. Now the truth was reaching the outside world. Now, because of me, the world was coming to know. And I didn't like knowing that I was responsible for their exposure.

Like "Bullseye" but with a Bird

July 11, 2008

With the exception of coal trucks and two-lane roads without shoulders, the eighty-mile ride from southwestern Illinois to Indiana was peaceful. I am realizing more and more that riding a bus for a portion of the trip really wasn't a shameful decision that we'd have to admit to our families and friends as I thought. The journey is about the journey—the flowers, the cornfields and the conversations with strangers. It's never been about New York. It was never about dipping our front tires into the Atlantic. It was always about the ride.

The roads roll like slow, afternoon ocean waves in Indiana. The sky is overcast. Les glides ahead of Aaron almost without a sound. He doesn't look over but Aaron can see him close his eyes and let out a sigh. "Yes," he mouths.

Trees appear upon the horizon. From afar, they seem to sprout from the earth like dark reeds. Soon, Aaron and Les are among them, their branches like arms reaching for the sky. But, before long, they are back on open, American highway again.

In Huntingburg, on the outskirts of Ferdinand State Forest, they find nine fast-food restaurants, two grocery stores, three gas stations and a public library. They have been without internet since St. Louis, which was the last place they looked for Couchsurfing and Warm Showers hosts. Aaron opens his computer and looks at the map he'd left open on his browser. "The map shows about ten more miles until this forest," he says. The restaurant is empty. Les is hovering over a chicken sandwich. He licks the barbecue sauce from his fingers and stares as the screen.

"That would make eighty. If we stop right before it I mean. What do you think?"

"There's a city called Birdseye."

"Birdseye, Indiana. Sounds quaint," he says, his teeth closing into his sandwich.

"Sounds like *bullseye*, but with a bird," Aaron says, crumpling up his trash and closing his computer. "Ha," he says.

No forest really begins anywhere. One almost always comes into one without fully realizing it. They are gradual gateways of greenery—trees get taller and denser as roads start to wrap and wind with more frequency.

Soon after leaving Huntingburg they are once again among the trees. Some are so dark that the setting sun in the west makes no shadow along the road in front of them. Within thirty minutes their surroundings are completely forested. In Birdseye, they stop at the first establishment they find, which is a Pentecostal church.

"Haven't thought of asking churches, have we?" Les says.

"Nope. Should we try this one?"

"Worst they could do is say no. But we're Christians too. Maybe they'll say no, but the fact that we believe something similar might help us a bit."

Aaron shrugs and says, "Yeah, I guess that's true."

Les leans his bike at the foot of the porch. He walks up and calls inside. Before long a man of about thirty appears at the threshold.

"Can I help you?" he asks, darting his eyes from side to side.

Les begins. The only difference in the story this time is that he mentions they both grew up going to church together.

The man looks at Aaron, then back at Les. "Sorry, guys. Ain't my call to make. You might have better luck at the Baptist church just down this way," he says, pointing south.

"Thanks," Les says, pulling his helmet strap tight under his chin.

The man walks away.

"Weird," Aaron says.

"Luck. Pshh." Les says. "Whatever. More like God's providence."

"Well, at least he pointed us to a different church. At least he didn't say to get the hell out of here."

"That would have been ironic."

The Baptist church is down a small hill on the left. There are big cars parked in the lot and a wide bus that is just leaving as they ride up. Old ladies with thick-rimmed glasses and white hair stare at them as the bus drives by.

"Hmm," Les says quizzically.

They enter the church and ask the first man they see about camping, but he doesn't know. Next, they ask an older woman, but she doesn't know either. Someone eventually points them to a man called John. John is washing dishes and says "what?" in a way that sounds as though he can't hear very well. He turns the water faucet off and dries his hands. Then, he turns. He peers around the room, finds the cyclists and walks up to shake their hands.

"Welcome," he says to Les. "Welcome," he says to Aaron.

"Thank you," Aaron says.

"Well, what brings you travelers here?"

Aaron tells him about riding from California and stopping off in Birdseye on their way to New York. Like Les, he shares a little about growing up in church too, which feels funny, as if he's bartering with his faith for a place to stay for the night. "But yeah, so we were up the street at the Pentecostal church and they pointed us here."

"Oh?" John says. He peers out the window as if to see the other church waiting outside.

"Yeah," Aaron says, following his gaze respectfully. "So, we asked about pitching a tent on their lawn just for the night."

"Oh," John says again. "Well, you can't be doing that."

"Why's that?" says Les.

"People might think it looks funny, and because everyone in this city wakes up and moves around before five in the morning. They'd see the tent in a churchyard and get nervous." John speaks earnestly. He has no reason to lie.

Aaron and Les nod.

"Well sorry, guys. Can't stay here either. I mean, I'd let you, but Pastor isn't here. His decision, you know?"

They nod and look around. Baby blue drapes, porcelain dishes hanging on the wall. A picture of a brown-haired Jesus.

"Hey," John says, suddenly looking at the floor. "Let me get my wife." He leaves the room and when he returns a gentle woman with a kind face steps in behind him. She is about eight inches taller than John.

"This is my wife, Diane. And what'd you say your names were again?"

They introduce themselves again.

"Said they need a place to stay, Diane." He looks over at his wife. "Told 'em they couldn't stay here," he explains. "Was tryin' to think of other possibilities and figured my wife oughta know better than me," he says, smiling.

Diane rolls her eyes and looks at them. "You look like you've been at it a while. How long exactly?"

"About two-thirds done," says Les.

"Hey," John says putting his hands on his hips. "Well, even California to Indiana is saying something,"

"Well, what about the rental?" Diane turns to John.

"Oh yeah, now we're getting somewhere," he says. "Hey, if you boys want to sleep over at our place we have a rental that's unoccupied."

They nod quickly. Three minutes later they are rolling behind John in his pickup truck. When they are out on the open road John seems to forget that they are on bikes and drops the petal to the floor. They joke about him not coming back, that he was playing a trick on them the whole time. They imagine John and Diane, if those are their real names, laughing together back at the church. Drinking decaf and slapping their knees.

Four miles down the road there is a turnoff. Trees and wet plant life cover parts of the road. If cars weren't regularly using it, the forest might wrap across and envelop it again as it had before man brought in dynamite, tar and gravel to make roads. John is waving to them at the turnoff, and he points to a house behind a row of trees.

John looks around the rental reluctantly, as if not wanting to step too far into it. As if there are memories inside he'd rather not think about.

Aaron swats a flea away from his leg.

"This here's the bathroom," John says, testing the faucets, his hand seeming unfamiliar with the calcified handles. He shows them the kitchen, the light above doesn't turn on. "Oh," John says. "No power. That's right." Outside, the trees are dark green, but inside the daylight shows a mint-green coat upon drywall that smells like it's been repeatedly dipped in a bucket of cigarette butts. Each room carries the same pungency.

Aaron swats another flea. Then another.

John is looking around at the front deck and shaking his head.

"Former tenants here?" Les says.

He nods. He holds his chin with his palm. His eyes tired, his face worn. He looks well into his eighties.

"Had a couple tenants here," he says. "Not too long ago they up and left without saying much. Didn't say anything actually. One day I'd come by to ask for rent and she got pretty upset with me. I told her that's okay, maybe tomorrow. Didn't want any problems, you know?"

They don't nod.

"They paid me twice, once when they moved in, and once the next month. But they was always screamin' at each other. I'd sit right there at my window and pray it didn't get ugly. Months three, four and five they never paid me. Just went on with things like I was just a pest lurkin' around." He looks down at his feet. "Oh, and they had cats, which is why you're swatting your legs so much. They didn't leave much more than a flea problem."

Aaron looks down and counts four on his legs. He swats them all away.

Les is consoling. He tells John that the tenants aren't his fault.

The old man nods and stares at the ground a while, distance in his eyes. He is somewhere, but not here in the rental. He has left it long ago.

"Oh but, hey," John looks up, "want to see my garden?" His back straightens, like the thought of his garden makes him a young man again.

They follow him down a slope to his long, new garden of tomatoes, lettuce, squash of some kind and two rows of corn.

"We don't know what we'll do with it all, but hey, sure is nice to have new life around here," he says.

Diane pulls up and looks across the property toward them. Her hand above her brow, she watches from the house before smiling, waving and going inside.

After dozens of tiny, red welts appear on their skin they ask John and Diane about sleeping somewhere else.

"Outside maybe?" Aaron suggests. "Or just on the porch?"

The elderly couple look sullen.

"We really appreciate your gesture," Aaron says. "You didn't have to bring us to your property or have us in your home. But you did, despite recently having a couple of rotten renters, you still took in two guys in need. I just want to say it means a lot."

John nods and Diane lays her head over his head in a way that would look funny if they were any younger.

"Come on," John says, smiling again. "Let's figure something out in the garage."

The evening sky is a show of lights. Clouds have bedded and covered it with purple and blue. The air is heavy, and they can feel it coming to rest upon their arms and faces. Beyond a row of trees in the distance the clouds exchange lightning like points of conversation. The four watch from the porch.

"These are my favorite parts of living out here," Diane says. A moment passes. Ten distinct bolts of lightning and then a long rumble of thunder.

She goes on. "It's chatter back and forth like the sky is speaking about something. We'll miss it if we're too busy I think," she says. "When we stop to listen here and there we find even the sky can take us away from what troubles us. Even lightning is a way to see that worrying ain't as important as stopping to consider the Lord and what he's sayin'." She looks over and sighs. "That's how I see it anyway, boys."

Explosions

"If we stay the course and always hit our eighty miles," Aaron is saying. "Then we'll make it. The question is, since we used to ride a hundred miles a day, what are we going to do now with twenty miles worth of time?"

"That's roughly two hours," Les says.

"Right. So, we gotta do more fun things."

"Like what? Museums, libraries, hikes?" Les's voice trails away as his gaze is caught by something. Both slow and stop at the sight of a large, red sign.

"Do you think it's real?"

"Only one way to find out," Les says. He dismounts and pushes his bike across the street, stopping in front of a large, black opening in the side of the mountain.

"Caves," Aaron says, examining the edges. The sign tells of several caves and caverns throughout the Appalachians.

"How's this for fun?" Les says as he rests his bike against the wall. He removes his helmet.

"I like this," Aaron says.

"Yeah. Me too."

Aaron follows Les into the cave. Gum, scribbles on rocks with sharpies and spray-paint and beer cans are evidence of the thousands of other visitors who have been here. The ceiling is thirty or forty feet high. The walls have natural stone juts and bulges to climb, which Les immediately begins to do. The cave wraps around a bend and disappears into darkness, no way to know what lies beyond without walking into it.

Aaron peers back and sees the sunlight curving around the corner like a hand made of white light. He brings his hand to his face and cannot see it.

Les suddenly yells: "This is our trip! We're doing whatever the hell we want!"

"Yeah!" Aaron yells.

"YEAH!" Les yells deep into the cave, his voice booming along the sides of the walls until, after several seconds, it can finally no longer be heard.

Before US Route 64 becomes more of a major interstate it is a serene two-lane road with greenery and dampened asphalt. Then, nine miles before the Louisville city center, it gives way to an eight- or nine-lane highway teeming with cars of all sorts rounding bends as if the edge of the city is some sort of finish line.

They push their pace. They round bends and coast descents, getting low and motionless for best results. They ride as though they are made for the highway—as if their muscles are blistering with strength to push heavy strokes across miles of automobile-only pavement and as if they're only seconds away from being arrested for doing it.

The first exit within the city drops them onto a road with a row of old houses with rusted metal fences used to distinguish property lines.

From this vantage, the city looks and feels a lot like St. Louis: older, lived-in, not exactly affluent. But the road that leads them through and toward the eastern part of the city feels like any inner-city road. Churches with white-stained walls and boards on the windows, convenience stores with broken pay phones, McDonald's on every other street corner and cars everywhere.

While looking on their map for places to use wi-fi, a man rolls up and asks them where they're from.

Aaron says, "Around Los Angeles."

The man says, "Woo-wee! That's a long way."

Aaron says, "Sure is, but we're enjoying the ride."

The man waves and says, "Well, welcome to Lou-a-vulle."

Aaron waves and turns to Les and says, "Lou-a-vulle, man. That's how they say it around here. Lou-a-vulle."

Les glances up, comprehending, and then looks back down at the map and says, "Lou-a-vulle. I like it."

Fifteen miles east of the city they replenish their food supply at a Kroger. From there, they plan to start knocking on doors. As they leave the parking lot a man on a motorcycle does the same from the opposite side of the street. He rolls by, waving, and then yanks back his throttle.

They wave too, cranking on their motor-less bikes like children behind him.

A quarter of a mile up, the man lets off the throttle and begins to slow. He pulls to the shoulder and sets his kickstand in place. His bike is a crisp red with chrome components, shiny as glass.

"Out for a ride today?" the man says as they approach.

"Yeah, a little one," Les says.

"Matt," he says.

Les steadies his bike between his legs and they shake hands.

"Where you get started?"

They tell Matt the story, trading off as they've learned to do. Les describing the grandeur of the beginning, Aaron the heat and lessons learned in Arizona and Colorado, Les Kansas and the bus ride, Aaron the beauty of backcountry Illinois and Indiana.

"Well," Matt says. "That's quite a trek." He removes his helmet and reveals a small face. His frame is short and stout. "So," he says before pausing, as if filtering through any number of questions and trying to find the one that will answer most of them at once. "Where do you stay at night?"

"Here or there," Aaron says. "Wherever we can sometimes."

"Campgrounds, Couchsurfing hosts, church yards, backyards, the sides of the road," Les adds. "You know, wherever."

Matt laughs. "You two really are adventuring. Nothing'll stop you."

"Nope," Les says.

"You have a place lined up tonight?"

"No, actually," Aaron says. "We don't. Kinda just thought we'd figure it out when we got tired."

"True nomads," Matt says. "Well, if you want, you can have my backyard."

"Done," Les says without hesitation.

"Alright then," he says, pulling his helmet back on. "Follow me."

His key makes his engine roar, he sets his blinker and the three make one large, train-like U-turn.

Matt's wife, Clara, is home and not expecting company, which is something Matt is aware of as soon as he sees the surprise upon her face when not one but three men walk inside.

They are a couple in their early forties and live well within their means. Their house has four bedrooms and a basement, all of which Matt later explains that he'd like to consistently use to host travelers.

"Like us," Les says.

"Like you. Never know who you might run into, right?"

"That's right," Aaron says, though he is thinking about it from the opposite angle. He considers his and Les's low-budget, piecemeal route, and the fact that most nights they didn't know where they'd be stopping. He considers how lodging was a planned-out idea when they began, but now, nearly three-quarters finished, they almost always arrive in a town, look around and just figure things out. They'd become true transients.

Matt shows them to the basement and says he changed his mind about the backyard. "I know you like the idea of camping outside, but I forgot something. A neighbor's boa constrictor is loose and, well," he says slowly, "you don't really want to wake up inside of one of those."

Aaron quietly scans across the room, checking for opened entry points.

Upstairs, the four share stories of growing up in church and how life as a Christian changes with the times. They eat cookies and pretend to see the snake several times at the window. Les pretends to feed a cookie to it and to pet it. Matt and Clara find Les a riot.

They ride from Middletown to Frankfort on what feels like rocket fuel, slicing damp air with their arms and legs. Bodies rested, kindnesses of strangers brimming, serenity unraveling, electric skies, southern-style mansions. They chant and sing, carving through the dense Kentucky forest:

THIS IS WHY WE CAME! THIS IS WHY WE RIDE!

THIS IS WHY WE CAME! THIS IS WHY WE RIDE!

"I can't remember the last time we've had a ride that we almost regretfully felt like we had to just push through." Les says.

Aaron looks over. The sun is near noon and poking holes into his helmet, beaming streaks of light on his scalp. "Yeah," he says, "those rides are so rare lately."

"That makes me really happy. None of it's owed to us. None of it. But we get it. We get to do this with our lives."

Before long, they are rolling into Lexington, where grand shopping rows, historic neighborhoods and college students fill the scene. It is like Prescott but with high-rises and older architecture. They fill their break time at a coffeehouse, reading, penciling in numbers in a sudoku zine and blogging. Long days and strenuous rides of over one hundred miles that only left time for eating, sleeping and getting up to repeat the torment again are over. Now, finally, they are on vacation.

"Your turn to start asking people," Les says, buckling his helmet together.

"Asking people what?"

"If we can stay at their place, or in their yards. Doesn't matter. I'm always the one to do it. Not that I mind. I just think you should do it too."

Aaron knows this has been true. *How hard could it be to introduce myself, tell the same story we've been telling for weeks and then kindly ask if we can sleep on their lawn?* But the thought that he would be imposing upon someone lingers like a black cloud somewhere at the front of his head.

They reel a few more miles in, and as soon as the city opens up into the country again they begin their search. At the first house, Aaron hesitates and pretends to need to park his bike along the fence perfectly. He hopes the person will simply open their door at seeing them on the sidewalk and invite them in. Or that they might drive up and say they could have the house to themselves as long as they wanted. Or, at least, that someone might blurt out that they weren't imposing, and that they were welcomed and invited.

He approaches the door, his shoulders drooped. He knocks.

No answer.

He turns.

"Give it time," Les calls from the sidewalk, his arms folded at his chest like a baseball coach.

"Yeah," Aaron says quietly, turning and knocking again.

This time someone can be heard inside. As the door creaks open, a tired old woman emerges and Aaron immediately regrets knocking. She has obviously been sleeping and appears to have trouble hearing what he is saying. He goes through their story at lightning pace anyway, knowing she will say no, or may not even know what he has said. At the end, she shakes her head and closes the door.

He comes down the porch and back to his bike, to the place he was sure he'd feel rejection set in. But it didn't. Instead, he felt indifferent, a small sense of confidence coming over him.

"See," Les says. "Wasn't that bad."

Aaron nods and points at the next house while scooting his bike away from the fence. "Next," he says.

He would ask two more people before a girl of around fourteen (who reminds him of an older Montana Fry from Kansas) answers the door and nods at everything he says to her. She is chubby and polite, but when it comes time for her to ask her mother about the two strange men who want to sleep on their front lawn, she yells, "Momma, get over here. Got a question from two men for you."

Aaron looks back at Les, who is already containing a smile.

The girl's mother looks disinterested and agrees to let them sleep beneath their tree as long as they don't mind the smell of pigs.

"Pigs?" Les says from the lawn.

"Yeah, used to have pigs. Just got picked up a couple days ago. Still smells pretty bad. But, you know, take it or leave it."

They take it.

The next afternoon, twenty miles before Grayson, Kentucky, something hard and round like a stone begins thumping through Aaron's back tire. Each rotation seems to increase the size of the bump, as if he were riding over a bigger pothole with every turn. Then there is a slight hiss—Aaron yanks on the brakes—and his back tire explodes.

Cars pass and Les sets Aaron's sleeping bag and camping mat on the edge of the shoulder so that cars will avoid them. With his wheel off and tube loose, Aaron knows this is no ordinary flat. "Did you hear it?" he asks.

"The tire?"

"Yeah, the way it wooshed and wooshed, louder and louder. Felt like riding over stones or something."

"Didn't really hear it, but I saw the way your wheel was bumping up and down."

Aaron examines the tube and finds a four-inch slit. "No way we can put a patch on that. Three patches strung together won't even patch that. How many tubes we got left?"

"Just one."

"I need it. We can pick up another couple next big city we're in."

"Good idea," Les says, pulling a plastic, oil-stained Ziploc out of his bag. He tosses the last new tube to Aaron, who carefully checks his tire for anything that might puncture the new tube. Then he pieces the wheel back together and they push their bikes a block up the road to a gas station.

As Aaron places the valve upon his tube stem he finds no gauge on the gas station air compressor. "Guess I'll have to eyeball it," he says.

Les shrugs.

When the pressure feels right he removes the valve and tops off his front tire, too, and in what seems like only ten minutes, they are riding up the road once more.

"We'll still make our host's house in Grayson," Les says. "Plenty of time."

Aaron's rear tire begins to woosh again as before. He quickly dismounts, leans his bike against a chain-link fence and says, "Oh, no—" looking at his tire before the blast sends sand and dirt on the ground a couple of feet outward. His ears are ringing; he silently stares at the wilted tire. He begins unloading his luggage from his rack again.

"Wait," says Les, having circled back. "Don't do that yet."

"Why not?" Aaron snaps.

"Because," Les says, "just do it at the gas station. We don't have more tubes so you can't do any work here on the side of the road. It's not safe."

"I know," Aaron says quietly, feeling his face getting hot. He pulls his bike toward himself, annoyed, and as his front tire rises and lands again on the pavement, a small hiss from it can be heard, and in less than two seconds the front tire looks just like the rear. *Heat and too much air pressure*, he thinks.

The gas station attendant tells them the nearest bike shop is ten miles back in the direction they came. Aaron doesn't want to ask Les to ride alone and for another ten miles, only to have to turn around and ride ten miles back. *Nothing could feel more imposing, he thinks. Nothing could feel more stupid. It was me who put too much air into them; it was me who could have bought more tubes if I had the chance; it was me who needed to go on this stupid bike trip in the first place—it's nobody's fault but mine. Now we're powerless and stranded.*

"I'll go," Les says, unclipping his bags and dropping them by Aaron's pile. "Just call our host and tell him we'll be late, and try to find a person willing to give us a ride to his house. I think it's only another twenty miles up the road."

"Okay," Aaron hears himself say. Before he can muster up a way to say thank you, Les is off, his legs cranking hard and westward.

Aaron asks every eastbound traveler with a truck if they could haul not only him and his stuff but also his friend who is not yet around but will be soon. Most drivers shake their heads and say no. He is surprised at how little he minds asking people for help now.

He finds a rhythm in telling the tour story, just as he and Les have done when knocking on doors. He begins in California and tells about getting all the way here, to Kentucky. He points at his bike, which is still unloaded, and he mentions that he and his friend only need to get to Grayson.

After about thirty minutes a skinny man with orange Bomber sunglasses and a mouthful of sunflower seeds says, "Yeah, man, sure. Just throw it all in the back."

Can't be that easy, he thinks. *Or can it?* The man sits in his truck, staring out at the road, both hands on the wheel with the engine off, while Aaron is loading the bed with his gear. *Maybe people do want to help people?* The man could speed off with everything he has. He keeps a hand close to the side of the man's truck, as if he might keep it from jolting back onto the road.

Inside the cab, the man asks, "So where to?"

"There's a bike shop to the west," he says. "I have no idea where it actually is. I don't suppose you do, do you?"

"Not too familiar with the area, but it's a small town. Sure we'll see it. No problem," the man says, starting the engine and shifting into gear.

Les is leaning next to his bike in front of the shop. A small white bag is sitting on top of his seat. He looks calm.

Aaron waves when they roll by and Les lifts his bike into the air and sets it into the man's truck and jumps inside. The truck U-turns, and fifteen minutes later they pass the gas station again, the crisis of two flat tires now a stupid memory to laugh about later. But around the time the road and all around becomes a blur, Aaron still finds himself brewing about the blowouts and wishing he hadn't lost his temper. Les is riding shotgun and is staring out the window.

The man says close to nothing, as if picking up two cyclists is perfectly normal to him. The only sound to leave his mouth besides the cracking of sunflower seeds between his teeth is the sound of him spitting them into a cup.

Their rideshare refuses gas money with the waving of his hand from his stick shift and drops them off at a resident housing complex at Kentucky Christian University. When they've unloaded the bed of the truck he spits seed shells from his window, waves and drives away.

David Berry, their host for the evening, is an introvert who looks at the floor or around the room a lot.

"What brought you to Kentucky Christian?" Les asks.

"Music," he says quickly. "And well, a teaching job. They were offering me a great deal so I took it." He looks at his brown couch.

"So you teach music then?"

"Yeah. I'm classically trained. They had an opening, so I applied," he nods at them.

"That's great," Les says. "And Couchsurfing? How'd you get connected there?"

Aaron is in the other room looking at David's fish tank.

"I took a backpacking trip to China once. I know it's supposed to be for more intense travelers, but a friend I hiked with had used it before, and I thought, well, why not? Sounded like a good way to meet people, too."

Les nods, and as they turn to talk about David's enormous goldfish, Aaron steps outside to replace the blown-out tubes with the two Les bought at the bike shop and David's floor pump. He is careful to only add ten pounds of pressure at a time and he double and triple checks to make sure the tires are on correctly.

Anxiety rises each time he presses the handle down and pushes air through the pump's chamber and into his tube. He watches his hands carefully, then suddenly remembers day one, pumping his tires up with his dad on the driveway. Homesickness begins to consume him; he imagines what kinds of bike rides his dad has been on lately. *How great would it be to take a ride with my dad right about now.*

When each tire is sitting at sixty pounds of pressure, he lets off and puts David's bike pump away. Remembering the sound and feeling of exploding air in his face from earlier in the day makes his stomach feel sour, and he can't help but feel like it is symbolic of the weird tension currently flowing between him and Les.

US Route 60 goes directly through Grayson and cuts north until it crosses the Ohio River, where it ends at US 52. From there, one can go northwest along the river, or south by southeast along the river as it curves and crosses into West Virginia into a city called Huntington. From Grayson to Huntington via this route, it is twenty-seven miles.

There is also an interstate going from Grayson directly to Huntington, avoiding Ohio entirely. On it, cars drive at highway speeds.

Five miles northeast of Grayson, Les and Aaron come to the junction.

"To Ohio!" Les yells and starts north.

"Wait, that's like seventeen miles out of our way. I looked at the map at David's just to be sure." He reveals the map to show Les. "See," he points, "if we go up the sixty we're making a big triangle."

"Yeah, but what other options do we have?"

"The interstate," Aaron says.

"Probably illegal here. What else you got?"

Aaron looks at Les. "That is what I've got, and we don't know if it's illegal. These are the only two ways, unless you want to roll through people's backyards. Your way is three times longer, so my vote is against that one."

"Mine's not. It's safer this way."

"Safer? For all we know your way could get us killed. What happened to risk?" It was an unfair remark, and he knew it the moment it left his lips.

"Riding on an interstate highway when you could ride on a back road is not risk. It's just stupid."

"Stupid," Aaron says quietly. He begins folding up the map. He would start riding Les's way. Not because he wanted to, but because giving way to people, and giving them the silent treatment in the process, was one of the better tactics he knew. It was an unbeatable move, because while appearing cooperative, it was an intentional way of one-upping the other person involved, as if to say, *Oh, is that what you think? Fine. We'll do it your way, but I'm going to punish you for it.*

Map tucked into his shirt back pocket, Aaron pushes up US Route 60 without a word. He can hear Les behind him. He is so close he can hear him breathing. He wants Les to just stop following him entirely. He can hear himself telling Les later, when they've finished the ride and are completely exhausted because of riding seventeen extra miles, *See, man, I told you so. Next time just listen to me.* He would be proud of that line. He smiles to himself.

Les sides him. "Hey Aaron, what the fuck?" His tone is sharp. His words, calculated. Direct. His face is squarely upon Aaron's.

Aaron falls back.

Tailing behind, in his mind he can see their anger finally spilling over. He envisions his feet dismounting from his pedals and his sight training up to Les; he sees him walking swiftly toward him. He sees himself hurling his helmet at the ground as hard as he can, Les spitting on the ground and then suddenly swinging. Them getting all tied up, drunken war buddies, throwing jabs into the air, trying to come down hard on each other, Les a trained wrestler, but Aaron with a six-inch reach on him. Them tumbling onto the shoulder, dirt everywhere. Les's nose bleeding, hair matted against his face with sweat and blood. No cars passing, Aaron standing, ceasing his advances and yelling: *There! How was that? Are you happy? Are you happy that it had to come to this? I know where I am going. You're not the only one around here with good ideas. You're not always right all the time either. Just because you act like life is perfect, and easy, and positive, doesn't mean that it is!*

Aaron shakes his head and can see Les pulling way ahead. Of course, he knows that Les is right. The difference between now and every other time Aaron has wielded his silence technique upon other friends is that he and Les still have at least one thousand miles to ride to New York. They still have weeks of sleeping in a tent next to each other. They still have five days in New York, a plane ride home and a welcome-home party to attend. They would always have this moment on SR-60, somewhere in northeastern Kentucky. They would have it to talk about for the rest of their lives.

I DON'T THINK YOU KNOW WHAT LOVE IS

After two years and nine months I sat in my Bug under a springtime jacaranda tree with its purple blossoms crushed now into the pavement by the tires of cars just like mine, and I had my elbows propped up on the steering wheel with my windows sealed tight and my cell phone pressed like a gun to my ear and my face buried in my arms, and the sun was pouring in through the windshield heating everything inside my car.

It was May 2007. I'd just returned from my first trip to Portland, with stop-offs in San Francisco, Monterey, Big Sur, the long Pacific coastline and so on. A vanful of friends. I'd just returned, and now I sat alone, weeping, fearing what I might have just lost.

I didn't want to believe that I'd been losing her for a long time. Despite the talk about marriage, despite enrolling in Bible college with the plan to do missionary work together, despite saving every dollar I could even with lousy tips and shifts being cancelled due to a roach invasion at the café, despite dropping those dollars into the same, old oatmeal container on my shelf in my room every night, despite planning to spend it all on a ring the very next weekend, here I was, in pieces all over Orange County, driving around without a mind, shouting, screaming at myself with the windows always sealed tight, the phone to my ear leaving message after message begging her to change her mind.

Technically, we were on what she'd called a break.

I was mad at myself. I'd overreacted the night we'd returned from the trip. I'd seen him in the dark at the back of the van wrapping her hair around his fingers as she slept. I'd watched in my powerless and horrified secret glances how he'd never fallen asleep but had positioned his torso ever-so-slightly in her direction. I knew then it all made sense. Everything I'd feared about the possibility of something going on between them was now coalescing. Back in Fullerton, I grabbed her keys and told her to get in her car with me. Now.

She finally answered the phone. I'd overreacted. I was sorry. So sorry. I was mean. Stupid. Childish. I was jealous. I was being him who'd let her slip from his hands into those of his best friend. And he'd caught her. Oh how he'd caught her.

"Why?" I said. The question we ask when we're not asking for an explanation, but pleading for a chance that has permanently passed.

Silence.

"Just. Why?" I said. I slammed my dash with my balled-up fist. I was so mad.

"I don't think you understand."

"Then make me. Please just make this go away. Make me understand."

"That's not how this works."

"How what works?"

"If one person in a relationship wants out, is it right to stay together?"

"Well," I said.

Silence.

"It depends," I said.

"No, it doesn't."

"It might."

"Aaron, I don't think you know what love is."

THE PURPOSE OF THERAPY
(PART TWO)

Alex looked at me and seemed to be thinking. It wasn't his job to sympathize with me, and I knew that. Actually, I was glad he didn't feel like he had to. It would have changed the experience in a way, and I would have thought of him less as a therapist and more like a friend.

"It changed me somehow," I said. I felt my heart rate beginning to quicken, and I felt as if I was opening up.

"How do you mean?"

"I mean—I mean people don't do this kind of stuff to people they love."

He was quiet.

"They just don't," I said. "This shit happens in movies, or in books, or just in anyone else's life but mine. Or at least that's what I thought." My face was mirroring the pressure I felt in my chest. Speaking was becoming difficult. My throat was closing and my voice was becoming hoarse. "I can't tell you how many times she said not to worry—but I still worried all the time and I never knew why," I said. "There was this hunch I had, do you know what I mean? It was like I knew all along but forced myself to ignore it. Do you have any idea what suppressing a gut instinct for so long can make you into? And then, lo and behold, my worst nightmare was true all along."

Alex let the room resound for a while. Soon, he said, "So your worst nightmare was that your ex really did want to be with your best friend all along."

"Right," I said.

Alex started writing again and I looked up at the ceiling. I was remembering vividly the day it happened. It hurt and I wanted to stand up and kick through the counseling room window. I hadn't forced myself to go there in a long time. I started remembering the person I became on the night I found out that my suspicions were true. I thought about telling Alex that part of story right then, the part after I'd grabbed her keys and told her to get in the car, the part where I drove ninety miles per hour straight to her house and how she was so angry that she got out before I put the car in park; about how she sent a text soon after that said, "I can't believe you"; about how I circled her block for the next forty-five minutes to make sure that he didn't show up after me. For some reason, though, I didn't tell any of this to Alex. Instead I said, "Somewhere deep down, Alex, before this happened, I think I believed that I could become the person that nobody would want to hurt. I learned it growing up, being somebody who wanted people's attention. And now, it's not that I think nobody's trustworthy, because I've been able to see past a lot of what's happened. But something has changed."

"How do you mean?"

"I mean," I said, exhaling. "I mean that these days I am less depressed by the event, and I guess I just feel more like I have this gaping, unhealable wound, and that every time I consider what I'm worth to the people I love, I feel its pangs. Just makes me wonder, you know?"

He nodded. "It makes you wonder what, Aaron?"

"If desiring affection and validation has just been a big waste of time."

Alex was motionless as he stared across the room. "Aaron, that question makes a lot of sense."

FREEWAY RIVERS

February 2008 — four months until departure

After therapy that day, I was blind to how the early spring sun shone, how it warmed the grass below my feet as I carried through it like a soldier. I didn't notice how blue the California sky was that day, nor how white its clouds. No.

I pulled my backpack tight to my shoulders and unlocked my bike. I turned right onto Nutwood Avenue and began quickly gathering speed, watching points in my rubber tires revolve below me like ferris-wheel seats. I passed beneath the California State Route 57 overpass and rode east for a long time.

I didn't know my hands were hurting until I realized how hard I'd been squeezing my handlebars. By then my back was fully hunched, my head was tucked between my elbows and the back of my neck and my shoulders were up like the ridge of an egg. I'd assumed the position for aerodynamics—to ride fast. I turned right at Kraemer Boulevard, rode over the Route 91 freeway overpass, crossed above the Santa Ana River and continued onto its bike path going east again toward the city of Corona.

Soon, when I was coming up on the outskirts of the city, I stopped to look back, as if to see a long path I'd created from the counseling center to here. But I didn't see anything but an empty road; nothing followed and nobody knew I was here. Nobody knew how badly I'd been needing to take the time to be alone with my thoughts, my prayers and the decisions I knew I needed to start to make. I don't even think I knew.

If nothing else had become clear to me during my sessions with Alex, what had was that the battle between me and my ex and ex–best friend had ended. Now, and for some time too, it was a battle within me. I'd spent most of the two years and nine months that she and I dated finding my identity in her. And when we'd broken up, I'd continued to allow her to shape my identity.

I had a real decision to make about my life. To continue to live as I'd been doing, cowering when they'd show up anywhere I was, or disbelieving my friends when they'd tell me I was looking more and more healthy, would keep ingraining in me the idea that I didn't have it in my to be anything but a victim. Victims feel afraid, and they are ruled by their fear; their actions and the way they compose themselves, and how they determine their worth in the world is always related to the fear they feel.

I walked my bike up a short trail and sat upon a ridge that overlooked the confluence of Routes 91 and 71. I watched it flowing east like a river (the reflection of sunlight off windshields, and the eventual occurrence of headlights upon highways is, for Southern California, the closest thing we have to real rivers. And we have many). I took out my journal and set it on my lap. The river of vehicles below me continued to flow as I looked at the old book in my lap, noticing its frayed edges and its scuffs and scratches.

At my back was a long hillside with new housing tracts at the top. With them was more newness, like fast food chains and grocery stores. Beyond the houses lay the Cleveland National Forest, Orange County's only real mountain range. They've always felt like old hills to me, mostly because of the way the mighty roots of many of their trees split asphalt roads and loom over them with low-hanging branches. Bikers used to rule a tucked-away mountain town somewhere within the forest called Silverado, but now its shops are dilapidated and abandoned. The forest itself will certainly undergo more change. It will never be the same, for all things must change, otherwise they die.

I wrote for a while and then tossed pebbles down the ridge and continued to watch the traffic with my journal open on my lap. It was dark now. I sat in silence for a while and thought about what I'd written.

I exhaled and felt good to have the ability to pray by journaling, good to have great friends and good to have the old mountains at my back. It had been nine months since she and I broke up, and it was good to feel that I had good things all around me.

I felt that I needed to rid myself of feeling like a victim, as if I needed to enact some ritual right then and there on the ridge overlooking the freeway. I wanted to feel that I was shedding old skin; I wanted to peel it off and throw it down the ridge and watch it land amongst the black overgrowth just before the freeway. It would be an act that symbolized freedom to start making new life decisions, freedom to ride my bike across America with Les after graduating from college without emotional baggage.

I felt around for the biggest rock I could find and came up with something the size of my hand. While I couldn't see everything about it in the dim light, all of its crevices, dirt and bumps, I could feel its weight in my hand. I could feel all that it represented.

I stood and brought my arm back. Then, I let the rock fly. It arced up and out, and then down, deep into the thicket.

Of course I knew that this act didn't make me fully healed and that I'd still probably wonder about my identity and my value as a person. That would all take time, of course.

But releasing the power that I'd given her, hurling it from my grasp and letting it fall far away, that was a symbol I needed to start moving on.

Part V.

Warm Cream Soda

Ohio comes and goes. They cross a mighty steel bridge and pass beneath a sign that reads:

WELCOME TO WEST VIRGINIA

Lunch is a cold, mechanical process: find a grocery store; park the bikes; buy meat, bread, yogurt and fruit; and devour all of it outside the store.

As they allow their food to digest, they rest beneath the grocery store awning. Cars pass, walkers look on. Les has his mat laid out as though he is ready to do yoga. He closes his eyes. After cleaning up, Aaron looks over the parking lot. His mind is a mill harvesting sustenance to feed the weird, knotted fire burning in his chest. When Les stirs twenty minutes later, they don't look at each other. They hit the road.

The body gets more adjusted to its conditions by the second half of any day. It is warm and at its peak, active ability. Aaron and Les streak across western West Virginia, covering the next forty miles of the ride in less than two-and-a-half hours, which, they figure, is their quickest stretch yet.

Charleston meets them on the outskirts of its limits as a slow-moving train headed home to rest. The city, while being the capital, is essentially a ghost town by only four in the afternoon. Public squares and shops are vacant, though most establishments are still open. They find a coffeehouse to see if they can get a Warm Showers host to let them stay a night or two. To their surprise, a man named Jason responds in twenty minutes.

"You can stay with me and my family all weekend if you want," Les reads part of the e-mail aloud. "All I ask is that during meal time we all pitch in. Otherwise, the place is yours." Les shrugs. "Sounds good to me, Jason."

Jason meets them downtown at 7:30 in sandals and shorts. They walk several blocks and he tells them the history of Charleston. "This city," he says, "and all the little towns around it, were once bustling places because of the coal industry. Miners dug coal out of these mountains for decades."

They nod. Jason's eyes are focussed. "Black lung," he says, "wasn't a joke. It broke this place all to hell."

They come back around to their bikes and begin riding. In all his audible thoughts and historical musings, Jason forgot to mention that Charleston has steep hills, and that they have to climb two of them just to get to his home. Aaron and Les, already changed out of their riding shoes, all but begin rolling backward down the first hill. Jason, with his clip-in sandals and no luggage, scurries like a mouse darting back and forth for new pieces of food.

They all laugh when they arrive at the top.

"I never tell guests about those hills," Jason smiles. "Figure if I tell a touring cyclist who has just ridden a hundred miles or whatever that he's got two more hills to climb he'll wind up sleeping in a ditch somewhere by the river. And this way I get to test your determination, too. See if the stories you tell me are verifiable."

"Well," says Les, breathing hard. "Do we pass so far?"

"So far," Jason laughs. He reclips and motions toward his home.

At dinner they meet Fran, Jason's wife, and Jenny, their four-year-old granddaughter. Jenny's mother, their daughter, needed a leg up after coming out of drug rehabilitation, Jason explains. "Having to care for her daughter while dealing with her situation was too much. So we gladly agreed to her request," he says.

Neither ask many questions about Jenny or about her mother. The fear of unearthing something not theirs to discover keeps the dinner conversation to meet-and-greet, surface-level types of topics. It would be up to Jason and Fran to let them in further to hear about their family's deeper story.

Still, Jason is rather open. "I have a son, too," he says later. "You may see him around here. He is depressed and spends most of his time in the basement."

"What's his name?" Les says.

"Kyle," Jason says. "He's a recluse." He scoops a spoonful of mashed potatoes into his mouth.

The image of a big, lifeless animal comes to mind, like a panda. *That can't be right*, Aaron thinks. *I bet he looks just like we do. He would probably be one of our friends.*

After dinner and dishes, Jason and Fran show them their Bike Friday folding tandem bike. Jason describes how riding one after using a traditional tandem for several years feels like driving the sports car of all tandems. "Like a dream," he says.

Fran tells stories of their two-month tour through Europe, and Jason explains that acquiring the tandem in the first place wound up being important for their marriage. "They say wherever you're going in your relationship, you get there faster on a tandem," he says.

Fran takes his hand.

Sunday they rest and go to church with Jason, Fran and Jenny. Then, after careening down the two hills, they return to the coffeehouse from the day before to read and catch up on the blog.

"Wait, what?" Aaron says, looking up. "You want to go dancing?" He thinks of Prescott and making dinner while Les danced with a couple old women in spandex.

"We are in Charleston," he says.

"Uhh, I think that refers to South Carolina. I think that's where the dance came from."

"Nah," he says. "Be back in a while." When he returns he sets the camera in front of Aaron and hits play. "Now, if that ain't the Charleston in Charleston, I don't know what is!" Sure enough, it is Les swing dancing with an invisible partner on the steps of city hall.

Something keeps Aaron from opening up or from laughing. *The longer I wait, the taller and more abstract the wall will become.* He can hear Les chuckling to himself as he rewatches the video. "Beautiful," he whispers through his laughter.

On Monday, they wave goodbye to Jason, Fran and little Jenny and fly toward downtown, where they cross over the Kanawha River and take one last look before approaching the Appalachians.

Ivy and low-hanging trees canopy the roads. The air is damp and the sun finds places to peak through. They ride up and down small hills like a music track on repeat, and midway into the ride, while passing through a small farm town, a small dog leaps over its barrier and into the road after them. A mixture of "Ah!" and "Oh crap!" lurch from their mouths as they click up their gears and attempt to pull ahead of the fixated animal. It nips at their heels but doesn't make contact, especially after Aaron pretends to bark at it. Les pulls ahead and takes out the camera. He tosses Aaron a stick and captures him turning the bike around and chasing the dog, who at this point has his ears turned backward and is sprinting home.

Inside a McDonald's in Summersville, West Virginia, there are more American flags than (maybe) people in the entire state. The wallpaper is one giant star-spangled banner, and every two feet there is a quaint saying about America painted upon a piece of wood. Pictures, toys, pins and other freedom-infused paraphernalia cover the dining area.

"We must be in Canada," Les says.

"Texas at least," Aaron says.

The cashier is watching them and rolls her eyes.

Across the highway there is a church at the top of a hill. Large orange flood lights fill an empty parking lot surrounding the church, and rows of southern-style tract homes no more than twenty years old run down the sides of the hill. Night has come and they ride up quietly, trying to bypass motion-detecting lights outside neighborhood garages.

As they lay out their sleeping bags inside the tent, a small, red car rounds the corner of the parking lot entrance. Two men are inside.

Aaron and Les freeze, like in Tonalea in Arizona, except now they have no deep embankment to shield them. When the car gets close enough that they can make eye contact with the men, it suddenly turns around and drives away.

"What?" Aaron says.

"Weird. At least we're at church," Les says.

Aaron watches the taillights disappear around the corner.

Les says something about how the cooking pot is their best weapon. "Come on though, man," he says. "Let's make some dinner."

Ten minutes later the car returns. Moving slowly again across the parking lot, it seems to take forever to cross and stop right at the foot of their camp. The passenger gets out. "Hey, guys!" he says with excitement.

"Hey," Les calls back.

"So uhh," he runs his hand around his beard, "are you the missionaries?"

Aaron looks at the tent and then back at the man, whose expression seems genuine, his mouth agape, eyes wide.

"No," says Les, pausing and then saying, "well, yes. In a way, sure we are."

"Well, we're just expecting some missionaries coming through town. Just thought you might be them. I'm brother Tim," he says, walking around his door and holding out his hand. He is chubby and his clothes are old. The driver gets out too but waves from the door. "That there's brother Alan."

"I'm Les," Les says.

"Nice to meet you, brothers," brother Tim says.

"Do you go to church here?" Les says, folding his arms.

"No. Not me. But he did," he looks back at brother Alan. "Not anymore though do you, Alan?" He laughs. Alan shakes his head and looks at the black sky.

Vague small talk goes on for a few more minutes. It is clear that brothers Tim and Alan are either totally messing with them, or that they are sincerely strange dudes with nothing better to do. Aaron glances back. *Wallet, phone, shoes*, he thinks, locating each inside the tent with his mind.

"Hey, well, I know you guys are gettin' all settled in so we won't bother you no more." Brother Tim looks at the tent. "But first, I have something for you." He takes his time and looks up at the sky while walking back around his door and then dipping inside. Brother Alan stands motionless, staring at them, nodding once. He makes a single sniff sound and wipes his nose with his hand.

Brother Tim emerges with a can in his hand. "Hopefully this helps on the ride," he says with a smile.

"Thanks," Les says, receiving the can and looking at its label. Aaron makes out the words and politely looks back to thank brother Tim too.

Then, with his arms suddenly spread wide, oddly like Jesus on the cross, brother Tim says: "Brothers, the good Lord provides! Remember it. Remember it for the rest of your lives." He drops his arms and backs up toward the car, extending his arms behind him to feel for the open door. "Well," he says. "Good night, missionaries."

Brother Alan smirks and gets back in on his side, and soon the red car pulls away again into the night. They watch its red taillights get smaller and smaller until neither can see them anymore.

"Was that real just now?" Aaron says.

"I think so. Yeah," Les says. "They were for real."

"You actually going to drink that?" Aaron glances at Les's hand.

"Cream soda?" Les says. "Not a chance. Plus it's all warm."

Aaron nods. It occurs to him that they've been standing in the same place for several minutes. "Probably been sitting in their car for a while," he says, "I wonder how long they've been looking for the missionaries."

"Might be cool by tomorrow," Les says looking at the can. "Do you want it?"

Aaron stares at Les.

"Didn't think so," Les says, shrugging and underhanding the soda into a trashcan by the church door. It clunks to the bottom. "Appreciate the gesture, brother Tim," he says. "But I have no use for your old, hot soda."

"Dude, what if there are actual missionaries also camping here directly on the other side of the church who needed a cream soda for something," Aaron says.

"Or," Les says, beginning to smile. "What if brother Tim actually does go to church here and is the janitor and sees that soda in the trash tomorrow?"

"He's gonna look down at where we slept, then out at the parking lot distantly and say to himself, 'Those guys weren't missionaries at all.'"

"They were just freeloaders!" Les yells. "And then, he'd crack the warm cream soda open and take a giant swig."

They lie inside the tent and situate their heads outside of it to look at the stars. The night is quiet now except for a soft breeze passing overhead and the flicking sound of bugs flying into the orange flood lights above the parking lot. West Virginia is still.

Soon, Les plays music from his phone. He mentions that a friend made him a mix before they left. The first song is "Cycling Trivialities," by José González, a song that Aaron knows well. *Especially relevant,* he thinks. He'd love to never speak of their argument again and to get back to normal on their adventure; he'd love to just go back to collecting stories across the miles together.

July 17, 2008

I get the feeling that the Appalachians are old mountains. They slouch outward like mounds. Their ruts and grooves make them look like they've been moved through evenly with a comb.

The Appalachian range is different than the Rockies. Its peaks are nowhere as tall, but its old hills go on for miles. Cresting one means rolling into a saddle and climbing another, and another, and another, seeming to repeat forever until one is already halfway across Virginia.

On the West Virginia side, the national forest is called Monongalia.

"Mon-on-gal-i-uh," Aaron reads a sign.

"Monon-galel-i-uh," Les says. "Monong-ela."

Eventually, they simply settle on calling the forest the Appalachian forest.

At lunch they find a rest stop with an outhouse, a table and a well. Aaron peers across the facilities. "This looks like the setup for a joke."

The grass below is wet from the dew so after lunch they sprawl across the table and try to nap. Soon, they hear a click. Then, another. And another. Aaron looks up. An old man with a fishing vest and a sun hat is looking at them and laughing to himself. Aaron waves.

"Les," he says.

"Yeah."

"We're being featured."

"Huh?" Les sits up in time for the old man to snap another picture while still laughing quietly, and after this second picture he walks on.

"Was he taking pictures of us?"

"Looked like it."

"Well, alright," he says nodding. "Damn straight."

The tiny town of Marlinton welcomes them with a bike path that leads straight into town. A café is the first establishment they see. It has a bike mounted above the door, like some kind of signal.

The shop owner tells them of a place just up the road where they can camp for free. She explains that Marlinton is right off the Appalachian Trail and that she gets backpackers looking for places to sleep all the time.

"The Appalachian Trail," Les says quietly as they sit. "I've heard of it but know almost nothing about it."

"Same with me. I wonder where it starts and ends."

"Can you imagine if we locked our bikes up here and just started hiking?" Les whispers, as if sharing a secret.

"If only, man," Aaron says. "If only it didn't come down to limited time."

After finishing their coffee and updating the blog they roll up to the camping area. A large awning covering an old concrete basketball court is directly off the path. Because of the dark purple clouds in the sky, they opt for the shelter instead of the exposed fields of grass.

In Marlinton, the West Virginian night is its own soundtrack of insects and animals. They watch the stars again for a while and silently drift to sleep.

The Home Stretch

July 18, 2008

The East Coast impending daily. We can feel it getting closer and closer every time we roll out our sleeping bags and peer up at the sky.

There is a certain amount of energy I feel that is compounding and blocking out all mental images and memories of hard times from earlier on. No amount of hardship clouds my mind when I am riding.

Life is funny like that, I think. I learn the most about myself at my lowest points. I know my character is built by strife and the process of being broken down. But completion, wholeness and wellness builds my courage and confidence. Strife and hardship build for me the character that other people get to see. But victory and completion build courage and confidence for myself alone.

Along the side of the road, Aaron spots a two-by-two-feet sign that has a cardinal sitting on a branch in the middle of it. Above the bird it reads:

VIRGINIA

And below the bird:

WELCOMES YOU

"Hey, get in this one," Les says, taking out the camera.

"Huh?"

"Swing across the road and get in the picture. Every picture is better with someone in it."

"Oh. Cool." Aaron puts a thumb up and mouths *cool* again for no reason while Les takes the picture.

"It was Tommy, I think," Les reflects when they are riding again. "It was he who said pictures are always better with someone in them."

"He once told me he never deletes a single photo he takes."

"Why's that?" Les takes another picture.

"Not sure."

"If I had to guess there's probably something to learn in every picture. Something to do better the next time around. Some way to improve."

"I had a teacher who said something like that. But he was referring to our exams. He used to say, 'Nobody ever really gets a hundred percent on anything. My grade scale ends at ninety-eight percent because you always could have done better.'"

"That's depressing."

"Yeah, I like Tommy's picture theory better."

Craigsville is another typical small, quiet town. There is a library, a fire station, a few churches and a market. It has one main road that runs west to east and connects to itself only small, country communities like Marlinton and Staunton.

They spot a Tastee Freez and pull over for hamburgers, fries and soft-serve. Then, with heavy stomachs, they look up and down the road for places to camp.

"It's not super crowded. Might get away with camp on the side of the road."

"Yeah," Aaron begins.

"No Warm Showers hosts around these parts. The only other option would be to ask someone."

"What about another church?" Aaron says, thinking of John and Diana.

"There's a church," Les points.

It is an old Baptist church that looks vacant. As they tug on the front door it suddenly swings open and unveils a terrifically bland and empty room. There are stained-glass windows along the top rim of the building, and each window is a different color. Brown, yellow, red and yellow again. One window is clear, giving the impression of having been recently replaced. The image of a stray football or stone, followed by a frantic dash away by a group of boys comes to mind.

Les is looking around the room and seems to tiptoe down the center aisle. "If anyone's here, they're probably in there," he says, pointing to the far side of the room toward an office door that says: PASTOR.

Les knocks and the wood sounds hollow. Then, he turns the knob.

"Hello," comes an old voice. "Come on in. I don' bite." The man inside has thick glasses, a crisp button-down collared shirt and a head of neatly combed silver hair. His office holds Bible commentaries and books on Christian living, some of which are familiar to Aaron from school. This man must be the pastor.

There is a must in the room that could only come from books, and Aaron instantly thinks of the offices of his professors and the counseling center. Memories fill his mind of conversations about theology and hermeneutics, and hours of attempting to understand events in his life with Alex.

"Yes, gentlemen, how may I help you?" says the pastor, wholly unsurprised. He is looking at them from above the rims of his glasses.

"Well, we're wondering, sir, if there might be a place for us to stay here at the church?" Aaron says.

He studies them.

"Not in the church, necessarily," Les clarifies. "Just out on the lawn in the back maybe. We've got a tent and sleeping bags."

"Right," says Aaron.

The pastor examines their attire. "So what's so special about stopping in Craigsville?"

They shrug and Les says they've just been going east for a while.

"From where exactly?"

"Southern California. Around Los Angeles," he says.

"Well, why didn't you say so? I've been there a handful of times. It's the kind of place that sprawls on and on. I drove there one time," he says, removing his glasses and staring at the wall in front of him. "I got through the desert and came through San Bernardino and all those places. I kept thinking the beach was right over the next hill. But it wasn't. Man, that was the longest hundred miles of my life," he says, leaning back and chuckling.

"Oh yeah, we rode right through it," Les says, sitting on a chair in front of the pastor's desk. "Took two full days just to get through what you were probably referring to."

As they talk, Aaron thinks of home again. He thinks of freeways and sunshine and old, boring city roads. His streets and avenues, simple as they were. He thinks of road trips to music venues with friends, and desert hiking to mine shafts; he remembers the ocean, blue from way out at sea, but green at the shoreline; of Brea, where he grew up; his family and his childhood street. Now, he is nearly upon the Atlantic.

The pastor points out the lawn behind the sanctuary and assures them they'll not have anything to worry about during the night. "Craigsville is a slow, sleepy town," he says, nodding and standing upright with his hands in his pockets. He looks at each of them and says, "Well, alright then. Goodnight, boys."

July 19, 2008

Trying to wrap my mind around the concept that we're actually riding across America on bikes. I really can't fathom it—it doesn't really seem real.

Aaron M. Green | 253

When we first told people about the idea most people just laughed with us. I remember thinking that some wouldn't believe we'd do it, and of course, I silently disbelieved we'd do it too. But then we went, and now suddenly days and weeks are passing without enough time to soak them in.

"Aaron," Les says. The morning sun is baking the tent. They've been awake for a while. On account of the Ohio argument, they still haven't spoken much. Mostly, they've continued to push forward. Les has his back turned as he says, "I'm looking at the map."

Aaron looks over to find it completely unfolded on his side of the tent.

"Oh yeah? Learn anything?" He yawns, falling back to his side. "Find out we're not actually in Virginia?"

"No. But something like it."

Aaron looks over again.

"We're going over our last mountain pass today. The very last of this entire trip. Remember how big of a deal that was when we were training?" Les turns and looks at Aaron. "Remember Big Bear and riding to Baldy and back?"

Aaron nods. "We got pretty serious. We freaking put rocks in our panniers and carried way more water than we'd need just for the weight. We had no idea what we were doing."

"And we didn't when we began either. We didn't a week in, and we didn't when we made it to Colorado."

"We didn't in Kansas when we decided to hop on the bus," Aaron adds.

"We don't even know what we're doing now. We're just doing it." Les turns to face Aaron. "I think there's something important to that."

In Charlottesville, their host is a young guy named Will who used to work for Habitat for Humanity. When they arrive and knock on the front door, there is no answer.

The house appears brand new and looks like a young architect's three-story dream home. When they go around back, there is a guy about their age with white sunglasses building what looks to be a back house. Before they can call out to him they are met by a barking Labrador.

"Felipe! No!" yells the guy from the roof. His tone is more alarming than the dog's. "No, Felipe!" The dog quits running but keeps his watch.

"Hey uhh...we're the Warm Showers guys. Are you Will?"

"No," he says. "I'm Ben." He sends two nails into the roof before coming down. He is shorter looking and more stalky on the ground. "Will's out but should be back soon."

"No problem," Les says. He gazes over the studio. "Did you build this?"

Ben nods and looks back at it.

"It's a fun project," he says. "Will's a good friend to let me help and I've needed a place to live anyway. I'm trying to save up so I can go on a cross-country trip. I plan to just drive and take pictures for my portfolio until I start running out of money. Who knows where I might end up. Maybe Oregon," he says. "But anyway, Will let me live here as long as I built him this studio. I love this thing. It's a loft above that looks down on the kitchen and living area."

"Amazing," Les says quietly.

They walk around the structure and each study different parts: Les the way the kitchen sits beneath the loft; Aaron the eastward-facing plate-glass windows; Ben the loft above.

"I'd love to live here, Ben," Les says. "This is great work."

"Oh yeah," he says. "Thank you. Well, hey, you guys are welcome to just hang out. I'm going to a screening of a documentary on the building of the Bird's Nest in China for the Olympics; it's at seven. I'm into documentaries. Love them actually. You guys are welcome to come. Might be fun."

"That does sound fun," Les nods and looks at Aaron.

"Thanks, Ben," Aaron says.

"We're pretty hungry so we might grab food first," Les says. "Got any suggestions?"

"Do you like pizza?"

"Who doesn't like pizza?" Aaron says, joking.

"Oh man," he says, getting excited. "Go to Brixx. You can get a beer and cheap, good slices too."

"Done!"

Just then they hear the studio door open. The man who enters also looks young. He has long, blonde hair and the way he walks is casual. "Are you guys the riders?" he says.

"Oh hey, Will," Ben says. "This is Les and Aaron." Ben is coming down the wooden stairway.

"Nice to meet you guys," Will says, ignoring Ben. "Let me show you where you're staying and then you can get settled in and do whatever you need to do."

Ben waves, and climbs the ladder again on the outside to continue working.

In the main house, Will shows them around. He talks about the kitchen, pointing out particular design patterns, and noting with pride three beer taps coming out of the wall.

"So, Will," Les says after they've walked to the front of the house, and after Will has shown them the three-story rock-climbing wall. "How much of this is you, and how much of this house was already here?"

"Well," he says, taking a blue climbing hold into one hand and pulling back on it as though to test it. "All of it was me actually." Aaron and Les look around. Everything feels newer and more worthy of note.

"Everything?" Aaron says. "As in, you designed and built this place yourself?"

"Well, I didn't put it all together alone. Did the most work for sure. But I designed it too." He looks down as though he's not really interested in talking about his house anymore. Suddenly, he points to a wraparound bookshelf. He pulls out one of the books and the shelf starts to slowly rotate, revealing a private bar. Upstairs he shows them the office that suspends in the air from the second level, and the three-story stairwell, each floor with its own passageway leading to a room.

Their room is on the second floor, and Will's is on the third.

"Well, sorry to bounce, but I have to go meet some friends. Make the place yours. Feel right at home," Will says.

"This place is legit, man," Aaron says, watching Will leaving through the back door.

"The dude worked for Habitat and got all his experience, got a loan, built a house, then a back house, and now he gets to live his dream," Les says.

"Think building the house was his dream?" Aaron says.

"Maybe, but a guy like that won't stop here. The sky is the limit." Les puts his hands on his hips. "Man, I want to work for Habitat and learn all I can and then design my own house."

Downtown Charlottesville has the usual college town vibe with coffeehouses, bookstores, pubs and art galleries all rolled into one. Brixx stands like any shop in the area: white walls, neon sign, patio in front. The pizza, on the other hand, is better than Ben made it out to be. Extra-large slices with fresh meat and combinations of cheeses. They eat quick and are up to get a second piece in no time. Beer in hands, fresh pizza and a downtown arts scene makes Charlottesville feel a lot like Prescott.

After dinner they find Ben at the library for the Bird's Nest documentary. Ben is delighted that they came and he quickly rattles off everything he knows about the structure already. "It's a nod to traditional Chinese ceramics, only with steel rods made with curves and openings meant to mimic an actual bird's nest." He uses his hands to emphasize just how it is able to fit over 9,000 people at once and his arms to report that it cost $400 million to construct. "And," he says proudly, "it became 11,000 tons and 7,811 square meters of usable artistry. Usable artistry! Can you imagine a piece of art that huge?"

After the film, Ben mingles, while Les and Aaron eat up refreshments and look around the gallery. Ben finds them and says he is glad they could make it and that while it may not have meant as much to them, to him, the documentary was gold.

"Oh, it was amazing," Les says. The two of them talk construction for a few minutes and Aaron looks out along the downtown walk. He peers back in time to hear Ben say, "But one day I hope to take pictures as well as those guys constructed art."

That's a great way of putting it, he thinks.

They settle in at Will's after waving goodnight to Ben, who, excitedly talking about architecture and photography, rode his bike back to the house with them.

"Les," Aaron says.

"Yeah?"

"Two things."

"Okay. Shoot."

"First, Ben and Will are a great duo. One has passion for days and the other has the skills to make things happen. Not that you're less passionate, or that I am less skilled, but it reminds me of us."

"Hmm," Les says. "I see that."

"Okay, second. There's a cat somewhere in this room. My eyes are like plums right now."

Les laughs, while Aaron looks for allergy pills.

After breaking out of the rolling hill country surrounding Charlottesville, they wind through fields where historic battles took place, some routes marked with signs that say "Civil War Trail." Beautiful countryside now laden with fresh grass and flatlands preserved to tell the history of the many battles (both here, and elsewhere) that led to the Declaration of Independence and the eventual freed status of slaves.

There is an Orange County in Virginia, just as in California, which seems fitting considering how close they are to the East Coast. But it is vastly different. These lands are lush, green and unadulterated by concrete and tract homes. Construction and expansion seem less a priority. Contractors have gone west. Aaron and Les pan across the country and wonder aloud about what life would be like had they grown up in this Orange County.

In Fredericksburg, they lean hard against a booth at a Wendy's and split dollar-menu items and watch the highway. They reflect, sharing brief thoughts about the trip. Completion is close. End is at hand.

They would be meeting a long-time friend, Paul, in a matter of minutes. Paul has spent a little over two years in the air force. He lives just outside of Baltimore where he is stationed. Paul can't tell his family or friends what he does for work, "unless you're okay with me having to kill you," he says, snickering. A natural genius, he tested into an elite program at the Defense Language Institute in California and has been training to decode cryptic messages ever since. Or at least, that is what everybody likes to say, though he'll confirm nothing.

A silver Toyota 4Runner glides through the parking lot and Aaron almost laughs. He hasn't seen Paul in over two years, but they've been close friends since sixth grade. It is comical to think of all they've ridden through—the desolate and creepy places like Sedona and Tonalea, or the lonely and open places like Eads or Olney Springs—and to find Paul pulling into a parking lot on the other side of the country, as if he was waiting to be called to come meet them.

Aaron is first to give him a hug and Les points the camera at himself and Paul when it is his turn to hug.

"Welcome to the East Coast," he says. "What do you think?"

Les goes on about how green and rolling this side of the country is and Aaron says it feels weird to know they are days from finishing.

Paul takes them on a short drive north to Arlington, a town just west of Washington, DC. He has arranged for the three of them to stay with his aunt for the night before taking another quick drive north to a small, mostly military town outside of Baltimore called Jessup. From there they would spend another night and day resting and enjoying a day off before making the final stretch into New York City.

"Dude, guys," Paul says, coming into the living room at his aunt's home. "Have you ever had Ethiopian food?" His younger cousins have made jungle gyms out of Aaron and Les by now.

Aaron turns with two children dangling from his body and shakes his head. Les does the same.

"Perfect," he says, and as he leaves the room he calls from down the hall: "DC—leaving in ten!"

Paul orders an enormous Ethiopian pancake-looking thing with dozens of small mounds of different colored coleslaw-looking things. They eat it all and pat their stomachs afterward. Tomorrow, they will become walking tourists, but tonight, they are simply friends of Paul, marinating in reminiscence.

They sleep in the next morning and around eleven Les yawns and says, "Oh baby." They pull their bags and clothes together, say thanks to Paul's aunt for having them, and head for the capital.

Washington, DC, at night is nothing like it is during the day. Dark streets with neon lights do injustice to the city's memorials, statues and grand public parks. There is so much to see—too much it seems. Washington, DC, is like Disneyland for the patriotic adult. Despite Paul's military background, and Aaron and Les's tour across the United States, none are very patriotic, and so they end up making ironic jokes about it. But they do make sure to see as much as they can, figuring that when you're in DC you see the things that make it unique, as opposed to simply hearing about it. From the Washington Monument (which Les pretends to hold up in a picture) to the Lincoln Memorial (which Aaron stands in front of alone, shrugging as other tourists stand all around him for their pictures too), to the Smithsonian National Zoological Park (Paul's choice), by the end of the afternoon, they've walked at least six miles.

Les says that walking this much is definitely working different muscles than riding does. Paul says that they've ridden across the country on their bikes, but by Les's logic, they still wouldn't be able to beat him in a foot race.

"That can't be right," Aaron says as they're walking back from the Smithsonian.

"Aren't you tired from walking?" Les says.

"Well, yeah."

"And haven't you ridden your bike across America, and doesn't that not seem to make any sense?"

Aaron thinks about this quietly while following Paul and Les who are attempting to track down the world famous Ben's Chili Bowl. *It would be nice*, he thinks, *and convenient to think that the accomplishment of a ride across America could mean the ability to run across it too.* But he knows that Les is probably right. Aaron wonders what running across America would be like, or walking, as Peter Jenkins wrote about in his books. The colors of the country are always different depending on how you cross it, and the reaction of people you meet is different too.

"Yeah," Aaron says, jogging to catch up. "Maybe I won't enter that marathon in New York when we get there after all."

Paul and Les roll their eyes. "Good idea," Paul says, throwing an arm around him.

If there was anything universally transferable that he and Les were getting from this trip, it is the knowledge that if they point their bodies east and put their eyes to the road, they can do anything. That is what a bike trip across a continent will do for you: it will make you believe that you can do anything.

Ben's Chili Bowl is a crowded, noisy, dirty place. And, the chili is amazing. A line out the door and stretching almost two stores down proved its reputation and made the wait well worth it. They are easily the only white people who've visited in the last hour, and the cashier gets sassy and jokes about something they're wearing just like she does with the older men in front of them and those directly behind them too. They are one of many in the hungry mass.

After lunch they drive to Jessup. They drop their gear off at Paul's apartment and drive straight to Baltimore to catch an Orioles game.

"We're on a bicycling trip," Les says, "And here we are going to a baseball game. I never thought this would be happening."

"Dude, it was all John and Pete. They're my buddies from around here. Thank them," Paul says.

Had John and Pete not suggested it they wouldn't have gone to Baltimore at all. They wouldn't have seen Camden Yards, and they wouldn't have come to learn that it's really not a very large stadium. Or that it was common to see people barbecuing and watching the game from nearby apartment balconies, looking unamused when the stadium's fans would cheer, or for another occurrence of "The Wave." They wouldn't have gotten to witness the Orioles win it in the tenth inning because of Luke Scott's walk-off solo home run either.

After the game they find a pub near the stadium and order beers. They cheer as if they were from Maryland with a sea of orange-and-black clad fans who've also found their way to the bar. Aaron high-fives a Cuban guy and looks back. Paul smiles and places his hand over his face.

Soon, they are back on the road to Jessup. Les comments on how weird it is that they've had an entire day of nothing related to cycling. "We've been at this how long?" He looks back at Aaron.

"Five weeks now."

"Five weeks," Les repeats aloud. He is watching the Baltimore city lights disappear behind him. "And in six it's all over."

"The home stretch, guys," Paul says, seeming to confirm their thoughts. "Almost home."

CHARGE IT

March 2008 — three months until departure

The trees along Nutwood by the university counseling center were sprouting again. In my final semester I had five upper-division courses, and while this class load wasn't ideal, I was willing to push myself in exchange for peace of mind while riding my bike to New York City over the summer.

Having put a few thousand miles between training and commuting on the Shogun since last June, I was beginning to notice how quickly it was getting battered. Its corners and components were getting rusted, it had two missing rear spokes and its derailleur no longer did a very good job of derailing my chain from gear to gear accurately.

I'd been talking to Les about buying a new bike for the trip, and since he was planning to get a new one too we started doing research. The problem was, though, that neither of us knew much of anything about new bikes.

"We'll need to start asking for help," Les said.

I didn't want to. Whether it was bags of pogs, skateboard decks or money to go to therapy, receiving has always been hard. Les, Tyler, Jared, Eric, Alex and many others had already given a tremendous amount of help over the last year. They'd tired over making sure I was becoming whole again. But now I was tired. I was becoming exhausted with feeling like I was always taking. I was wanting to finally be able to open up and start giving again.

"Really?" I said.

Les looked at my sideways. "Yeah, why not?"

I shrugged.

"We're going to have to get used to it. We're going to be asking people for help all the time on our trip."

I shrugged, but I was hoping he'd be wrong. In my mind was the image of two cavalier cyclists with beards, hunting for their food and camping in the woods every night. I thought it could work.

"I might go get a membership at REI and get a bike there," Les said. "I suggest you do the same, unless you know anybody who can help you find a bike."

I did, actually. "Well, I have a friend named Carter in one of my classes. He works at a shop and can probably make some recommendations."

"Great," Les said. "Ask him, and tell him about our tour. Maybe he'll give you a discount."

The audacity. I hated the idea of treating people as opportunities to step up in the world. Or at least that's how I saw it. I knew somehow, though, that I needed to push beyond whatever pride or fear of rejection I had in not asking for help. The next time I saw Carter in class I waited several moments before finally asking him about bikes.

"What kind of riding?" he said.

"Well, it's for a tour, actually. This summer I'm planning to go coast to coast." I was embarrassed about telling him I would be riding 3,600 miles and didn't know the first thing about bicycles.

"Oh, how fun," he said nonchalantly. "But my shop doesn't carry any touring bikes, mostly because people in Orange County don't tour that much. Generally," he said, shifting in his chair, "touring bikes are lower to the ground and longer. Which," he said emphatically, "helps with stability when carrying heavier loads while on tour. Do you want me to look into ordering you a touring bike? I'll even build it up for free. I need the practice anyway."

I couldn't believe how willing Carter was to help. I didn't even have to coax him with money or a sob story. I was trying to listen to Les, and in the end, I didn't like that I was being so averse to help. "That'd be great," I said. "But how much should I be budgeting?"

"How much do you have?"

It felt like an awkward question, mostly on account of my pride. "I have about a thousand. Will that even be enough?" I was actually unsure as to where I would get the one thousand dollars, because at that point I had only saved eight hundred from my tips at the café. More important than money for a bike, though, was my need for that eight hundred to go toward food and supplies while on the road. Where I even pulled one thousand from is a mystery, but Carter shrugged and told me he'd see what he could find.

A week later, he came into class with a printout displaying a bike, the Long Haul Trucker, made by a company called Surly.

"It's the best touring-style bike in your price range," he said. "You won't be disappointed. Not a chance."

I had little else to go on, so I decided to take him at his word. "Alright, man, order it up."

When I left class that day, I felt myself beginning to panic. I had no savings and plenty of school debt. As I rode the Shogun home that afternoon I forced myself to take a deep breath. I whispered a prayer as I let the air roll back out of my body. I knew I'd need to buy the Surly on a credit card, even though once I began the trip I'd have no income, and therefore no way of paying off the debt. I'd just have to chance it.

Success

The road out of Jessup, somewhere along Pulaski Highway, cuts straight through Baltimore and curves northeast, resembling any ordinary highway in any state. Asphalt lanes, concrete shoulders, billboards, call boxes and suburban exits that lead deep into the surrounding hillside communities. Drivers hug shoulder lines close, giving Aaron and Les quick spooks as if they're playing some sort of sinister game. The weather is a balmy ninety-five degrees.

After two and a half days of not riding, their hunger for the road feels insatiable. They give in to the temptation to push hard and bite off long, fast stints that their legs and lungs may not be ready to swallow. But they push anyway, and they end up wringing a quick eighty-two miles out of themselves.

Twenty miles before Wilmington they arrive at the edge of a port city called Havre de Grace and are immediately met by a big white sign:

CARS ONLY
PEDESTRIANS STRICTLY PROHIBITED

Les checks the map to look for another way across. He finds that the nearest pedestrian bridge is ten miles up, which, of course, translates to ten miles up and ten miles back down to their route just to bypass a five-hundred-foot-wide channel.

"Well, what do you think this time?" Les says plainly. His question cuts a little, Ohio ringing a little in his words.

Aaron looks up from the white bridge. He wonders why Les doesn't just make the decision, since the last time they'd argued about directions they'd ended in cold dissent. He looks down the road, as if to see the alternate bridge ten miles away. He shrugs, knowing just as before he'd rather chance it and just cross the bridge in front of them.

"I mean," Les says, looking across the river and at the cars passing and picking up speed across the bridge, "it's not very far, right? We've crossed a ton of these. What makes this one so special?"

They watch the great white passageway in silence. Aaron wants to bring up the amount of time they'd save, but he doesn't. Something about wanting to remain in a place of mending with Les keeps him from speaking his opinion.

"Screw it," Les says. "Let's go."

They pull out after a string of cars have passed and the traffic signal behind them has changed to red again. They fly and watch the blue waters of the Susquehanna River flowing toward the Atlantic beneath them. The only object on their right is a three-foot concrete barrier that lies almost on top of the white shoulder line. They take up the rightmost lane together, pumping and pulling. Cars from behind are approaching and they can almost hear the annoyed thoughts of motorists whose car engines cut back, and then rev high as they pass in the leftmost lane. Aaron looks into their windows as they pass. Most drivers don't look, but some do. Some glare.

On the other side of the bridge they roll to a stop at another traffic signal. Blood is throbbing their temples, adrenaline pulsing their veins. With one foot off his bike, Les scoots over to Aaron and gives him the hardest high five all trip and yells: "WOO! Hell yeah, we did that! Hell yeah!"

A police siren ahead. They can see from half a mile away how the officer tears around cars and across traffic lanes.

When he gets to their intersection, he pulls into the middle of the road and abruptly stops. His lights are still flashing and his siren echoes all around. They and the cars around them now have a green, but none move. All watch as a pale white officer from inside the cruiser points and motions violently toward the side of the road. Aaron looks left at the car next to him, then back, and the officer shakes his head. With charisma, he points right at them and then firmly to a gas station parking lot right off the road.

"Oh," says Les, and they begin moving off the road. In the lot the officer moves in behind them as though herding sheep. Aaron takes out the camera. Carefully positioned, he snaps a picture from through his arm while his back is turned to the cruiser. The preview shows Les shrugging and smiling. Behind him the police cruiser reads *Perryville/Charleston Police* on the side.

The officer steps out and hikes his pants, like in the movies. He is even chewing gum. "Just what in the hell would make you do that?" he yells, throwing his door shut.

Aaron considers sharing that they would have had to ride an extra twenty miles by going around the bridge. But he doesn't. He sees the rhetoric in the officer's question as soon as the pale man in his navy uniform with two sky-blue stripes down the side pulls out his ticket book and rifles toward the end of it.

"Ah shit," Les says quietly.

Aaron feels responsible. *This is why you follow the rules; this is why we go around; this is why we ride twenty-seven miles out of the way instead of riding on the interstate.*

"I don't think you understand," the officer says quickly. "You're not supposed to be on that bridge. Bikes are never supposed to be on that bridge."

Aaron wants to laugh a little. *Yeah, dude, no kidding.* All they can do is shrug and say sorry as he takes their IDs. He walks back to his cruiser and sits inside. The nearby intersection flows again like normal. After a few minutes he returns. "I don't know how California does it, but out here we're safe and we're secure. I've decided that I'm not going to write you up but don't you dare do it again. Don't even think about it. You won't be warned next time."

Les looks at Aaron. His face is plain, but his eyes say everything. By this point the officer's face is pink and sweat is beading into his eyes and he is trying to wipe them out between the words he's saying to them. The officer says, "Well, do you got that or what?"

Aaron nods and feels himself relax. He looks down, over his handlebars, and then back at Les, who has his hand covering his smiling mouth.

"Yes, sir," Les says.

The officer looks at him almost sideways and chews his gum in the front of his mouth. "Good." He gets into his car and drives off.

They ride on, laughing their entire way up Pulaski Highway. Les rides with no hands and yells: "We're safe and we're secure!" Aaron smiles alongside, shaking his head all the while.

Their contact in Wilmington is a high school shop teacher named Jimmy. Also a proud cyclist, Jimmy meets them at his door wearing spandex and a baggy jersey. Before he properly greets them he, in all his excitement, goes straight into all of the arrangements for eating, sleeping and relaxing that they could do that evening.

"Well, you know what... Hey, you guys can stay as long as you want," he says, looking them in the eyes. "You can—you can eat here, or, or, just sleep, whatever you feel like." He is a bigger man, but the definition in his calves shows his dedication to the bike.

"So I got, I, I got hit once," Jimmy says when they're all seated at the backyard table. His fiancée, Monica, brings a tray of snacks to the table. "Eh, you want a beer?" Jimmy says looking at them.

"You know, that sounds great. I would, thank you," Aaron says. Les shakes his head.

Monica smiles and returns to the house.

"Well, anyway, I got hit by this guy over here. He was merging over and—wham!" The way he yells seems to make his windows rattle. "Right into me!" he all but screams. "Man, what a surprise that was." He smiles to himself and sips his beer and Monica returns with a beer for Aaron.

"We were so worried," she says, sitting in Jimmy's lap. Her accent sounds like New Jersey from all of the movies.

"Yeah, yeah, but no hospital bills, fortunately for me. Or for him," she says. Jimmy laughs and sips from his beer.

"But I did make 'em buy me a new bike because mine got pretty torn to shit. New shoes too," he says, pointing to his doorstep where they are sitting. They are clean and bright. "Hey," he leans in. "You wanna swim?"

"Oh, I'd love to," Les says quickly.

Jimmy looks excited and starts to get up. Monica has to leap off him first. He points toward the door again. "Towels in there, my friend. No problem." On his feet now he says, "Oh, hey wait. You guys wanna see something really cool?"

They both nod and Les follows with, "Of course we do."

Jimmy laughs. "It's a non-negotiable, really. Wouldn't have let you stay if you didn't." He sets his beer down. "Here, follow me."

Down a set of steep, creaky steps into the basement, Jimmy flicks on a light. They are in an eight-hundred-square-foot room with nothing but a washer and dryer and a tiny world surrounded by train tracks.

"A train set?" Aaron says. Almost immediately, he feels condescending. He looks at Jimmy who has just pulled on a conductor's hat.

"Oh, like you've never seen," he says. "Come over here."

"It's a city," Les says, stepping around the table display slowly.

"My pride and joy," Jimmy says. "It used to be that I'd build this world when I was bored. Actually, I got it after my first wife died. That's when I really started building, and one thing led to another, and I found myself down here as often as I could be."

There is a *choo-choo* sound and soundtrack of a locomotive chugging down a line. Then, another *choo-choo* and above they see a track has been built along the ceiling that zigs around in a figure eight.

"Multiple cities!" Les says.

Jimmy is still, holding his large controller; he watches his trains like a child in a dream. He is a creator, a visionary, a master, and he makes his little world go around and around.

The next morning Aaron creaks up the wooden basement stairs and finds Jimmy hard at work in the kitchen. There is coffee on and Monica is gathering dishes from a cupboard.

When Jimmy sees him he tells him to sit and asks him if he rested well. But before he can answer Jimmy asks how he feels about some secret pancakes.

"How secret are we talking here?" Aaron jokes.

"Only the best kind of secret," Jimmy smiles. Monica nods at Aaron approvingly, as if to say that the pancakes are going to be just fine.

"You like some coffee? You drink coffee?" Jimmy asks.

"All the time. Yes. Thank you. And yes, I'd love some secret pancakes and, yes, my sleep was great. With the kind of riding we do it's kind of hard not to sleep well, you know what I mean?"

"Oh, I know. Believe me, I know. Those long rides will get you." Jimmy's voice is trailing off. He is distracted by pouring his batter on the skillet. Monica brings a cup of coffee over.

"Milk or sugar?"

Aaron holds up his hand and shakes his head as he sips. "But thank you," he says. As she returns to the kitchen he tries to find the exact New Jersey movie that she reminds him of.

"You read?" she says, coming back with her own cup. Jimmy looks up to see Aaron's response.

"Yeah, I love to read. Fiction, biographies, philosophy that I don't understand," he says and smiles.

Jimmy smiles too. "I'm not much of a reader at all. But she, wow. Let me tell you, brother. She could read every hour of every day and would be the happiest woman in the world."

"Oh stop," she says. "But he's right that I love to read. I'm actually a teacher," she says, sitting down. She turns to Jimmy. "Hey betcha didn't get to telling them that when you were looking at the trains now, did ya?" She peers back at Jimmy. He looks sheepish.

"What do you teach?" Aaron sips.

"English, mostly. But I'd love to move solely into teaching literature. I just love the greats."

"I began as an English major, actually," Aaron says.

"Really, that's wonderful," Monica says. "What were some of your favorite classes?"

"Two stand out for sure. One was an intro to creative writing, and the other was a poetry class, which was also an intro now that I think about it."

"Did you read much Emerson?"

"Yeah," Aaron says, thinking. "'Ode To Beauty,' right?"

"Yes," Monica nods excitedly.

"That's all I can remember." He laughs.

"That's alright! Hey, honestly, I was reading your and Les's trip blog. It is really inspiring."

"Thank you."

"You're making me look bad too," Jimmy says, smiling and bringing the first round of secret pancakes over. "Now I'm gonna have to get out there and prove myself too!"

"Oh stop," Monica says.

Les steps into the room from the basement. "Morning," he says.

"Good morning, Les," Jimmy says. "We were just about to start eating without you." He smiles.

As they eat they talk about family and friends and Jimmy talks about his son. "He's an amazing young man. I love him to death. Let's see, right now he's doing the community college thing and is working as a bouncer. Ha! You might never think you'll have a kid who wants to push people out of rooms, but then when it happens you look at him and you feel really proud."

"That's really awesome, Jimmy," Aaron says.

"Is he around today?" Les says.

"No," Jimmy says. "He works late at the club, and then goes to school early. The kid works really hard."

Monica has her hands around her coffee cup and is watching Jimmy speak. She, whether she knows it or not, has a small, contented smile on her face.

"That's really inspiring," Les says, "that you love your son that much." It is the kind of comment that cuts a bit deeper into a table conversation. The kind with the ability to end all talk on the subject in a heartwarming, reflective kind of way, or to move it deeper. Les has always had a knack for this.

"Thanks, brother," Jimmy says, midbite. "Thank you for saying so."

As they're packing, Jimmy is explaining how best to get to Philadelphia and up to New Jersey. "From there," he says, "You'll see the signs everywhere. All roads lead to Manhattan," he laughs. "That's how the saying goes as far as I'm concerned."

They load their bikes and pull on their helmets.

"Mind a picture with us?" Les says, pulling out the camera.

"Of course not," Jimmy says. Monica leans in and Les and Aaron stand on their sides. The camera blinks its usual red and then flashes white at their smiling faces.

"Thank you," Jimmy says, "and I know that sounds sort of weird—hey, you should be saying that to me!"

"Thank you, thank you, thank you," Les says, laughing and putting his arm around Jimmy's neck playfully.

"Just that you came and were such cool guys. Man, that blesses me. I don't know if I believe in God much, never really have much, but hey, I'm blessed all the same."

"I want you guys to take this too," Monica says, stepping up. "All of my colleagues would burn me at the stake, but I don't care. This is a poem that has probably erroneously been attributed to Emerson. It's called 'Success' and whether it was him or not, it reminds me of you, and I want you to take it with you into your last days of the trip."

"Thank you, Monica," Aaron says. "We'll read it together and often."

She smiles.

"Two days and one night!" Jimmy says. "Make them the best days you've ever ridden because they're definitely going to feel like 'em!"

As they ride from Jimmy and Monica's home, turning a corner and watching the trees from their street disappear behind other trees and homes, they exhale separately and don't speak much for a long time. Their gears crank, and their wheels turn, over and over, covering now the newest ground of their trip as they follow Governor Printz Boulevard north toward Philadelphia.

Just outside Philadelphia, Aaron feels the air in his rear tire suddenly flood out. When he inspects it, he finds a screw head half the size of a dime firmly planted in his tire.

"Well, it could be worse," he says.

"It's been a while since we've had a flat," Les says, reflecting. "Last was Kentucky. We're two riding days away from New York and I can't believe we've managed to pull so few flats. Your tires have a knack for exploding, but still, the true, natural flats, because of a thorn or a wire in the road, have been scarce."

"Almost seven thousand miles between us, and we've only had six or seven flats."

"We should record ourselves saying this and send it to the companies who make our tires. Maybe they'll put us on the radio and send us a fat check."

"That makes me wonder why we didn't try to get sponsors in the first place."

"We talked about it."

"We did?"

"Yeah, at the same time that we talked about raising money for a cause or something. In the end we decided that this just needed to be something we did."

"Not like us giving something back, but more like us receiving something."

"Yeah," Les says, thinking and watching Aaron pull the screw from the tire and begin to patch his tube. "I think that's right. This was a trip for us to receive a lot. Maybe we've given of ourselves here and there."

"Feels weird though, you know?" Aaron says, studying the tire. "My faith has basically been based on what I've given back. I mean, seriously. Feeding poor people, hanging out with friends, coffee with people interested in Jesus but who hate church."

"Oh yeah, me too. It's good to remind ourselves that who we are and where we are today is because of what we've received, not because of what we've given."

"I think I'm gonna use that line as my own someday," Aaron says. "Thanks in advance." He smiles and sets his wheel back into his frame and pulls the brake cable into place.

At the heart of Philadelphia is a four-thousand-square-foot roundabout that entraps city hall. From there, directly northwest is one of only a few diagonal streets in the city (and definitely the longest). Benjamin Franklin Parkway starts at city hall, passes JFK Plaza (known to locals and skateboarders alike as LOVE Park), goes straight through Pennwalt/Levy Park, passes a number of hotels and the Cathedral Basilica of Saints Peter and Paul, swings around another roundabout at Logan Square, crosses over the Vine Street Expressway, and branches off into a number of different arteries around the Philadelphia Museum of Art, otherwise known as "The Rocky Steps."

"We have to," Les says as they roll up.

"Oh I know."

"No, really, we have to do this."

"And I'm telling you I agree," Aaron says, pulling ahead slightly.

"I don't know if you really do," Les says, catching up. "Do you know how much this will mean to our blog if we reenact Rocky running up the steps?"

Aaron pretends to think about it and smirks. "So, can I be Mickey?"

"Yes, yes, yes," Les says, matter-of-factly. "Obviously you have to be Mickey."

The steps are plain as day and impossible to miss. Aaron thinks of the dozens of times he watched the Rocky movies growing up and can't believe he's actually in front of the steps. They look smaller, wider, and a statue of Sylvester Stallone as Rocky is off to the side under a tree.

They lock up next to Rocky and joke about how maybe they should be locking up to his big steel leg. Les stands next to the giant steel frame, with its mitted hands in the air, and he points at his own leg muscles while Aaron takes a picture.

"I'd like to see Rocky ride across the country," he says staring upward. He walks toward the steps. "Okay, so here's what we'll do. I'll be Rocky and you give me a pep talk as I'm trying to run up. I'll pretend like I can't make it but you just have to keep me going. Sound good?"

"I can do that." Aaron flicks the camera on. As it pans across the skyline there are cars and runners making their way toward the steps. Aaron turns the camera so it lands upon them. He has his hat facing forward and Les is sitting next to him.

"Oh, hi," Aaron says.

"Hey," Les says.

"So, here we are at the Rocky Steps and you'll never believe who we just saw."

"Never believe it."

"We saw Rocky and Mickey out here training," Aaron says. "And uhh, well, actually, here they are." He turns the camera three hundred and sixty degrees and when it lands on them again he has his hat backward and Les is stretching out against a wall.

Aaron does his best Mickey impression, which, midimpression, he realizes is actually an impression of the exaggerated version from the Brisk iced tea commercials.

"Hey, man, ya know," Les starts running up the steps. "I can do dis."

"Get up der, Rock!"

"Hey, man, yeah, I can do dis!"

The camera bounces with every step Aaron takes. "Come on, Rock, you sonuva... Get up der an' make me proud!"

Les pretends to struggle halfway up. "I don't know, Mick."

"Get up there, Rock! For your children!"

"No children yet, Mick," Les pretends to almost fall, his muscles at peak exhaustion. "No children!"

"The kids, Rock, you gotta have kids."

"Gotta have kids, Mick. Gotta have kids. Gotta have a wife! Gotta get married. I gotta get married, Mick!" He is almost at the top, he is pretending to breathe heavily.

"Almost, Rock. For the wife and kids!"

"Alice!" He yells, trading the name Adrian for his girlfriend's. "Aliiiice!" He raises his arms to the air as he gets to the top and Aaron pans the camera around him as in the movie. "Aliiice!" Les yells again.

A jogger coming up the steps shakes her head and starts back down again.

Aaron clicks the camera off. They watch the skyline for a moment.

"Want to get a Philly cheesesteak?"

"Oh, you bet I do." Les says.

Sixty-five miles to New Brunswick in New Jersey tonight, and then twenty-five miles to the ferry at the northernmost point of Staten Island tomorrow. From the moment they board the ferry, there will be no more bike riding needed in order to get to Manhattan. Southern California to New York City, one day away.

It is eleven-thirty in the morning in Philadelphia when they mount their bikes again, roll back down through Logan Square, turn east onto Race Street and catch North Columbus Boulevard and head northeast along the Delaware River toward New Jersey. The roads are mostly open at this time of day and they crank at around sixteen miles per hour.

Finishing the tour is beyond them. It is nothing they're ready to know how to handle—it is both nothing and also everything they have prepared for. They have been like workers at the plow for thirty-nine of the longest, most inspirational days of their lives. Their duties have been to eat, cover ground, carry their belongings, meet people and sleep. They've accomplished it all, and they've already experienced success. Not because they rode their bikes the whole way, nor because they did it in the amount of time they planned to. It will be a success because they simply decided to have an adventure that summer. From the moment they pedaled away from the pier in Huntington Beach it began.

They follow US Route 1 wherever they can and depart from it at the southern part of New Brunswick at Jersey Avenue. From there they begin to slow their pace and take the city in. New Brunswick is home of Rutgers University, which neighbors much of the city's portion of the Raritan River, an eastward, wiggling channel that finally meets the Lower Bay beneath Staten Island and Brooklyn. This water is part of the Atlantic Ocean.

Their host for the night is a college student named Rick. Les calls when they are fifteen miles out, somewhere near Princeton University, but Rick doesn't answer.

"Well, I guess we'll just play it by ear," he says.

"Nothing we aren't used to."

They ride along and soon Les gets a text message responding to his voicemail. It reads:

HEY MAN, YOU'RE FREE TO COME ANY TIME. THERE'S A TENT OUT BACK, BUT YOU CAN SLEEP WHEREVER. MY ROOMMATES ARE HOME, BUT I MIGHT NOT GET HOME TIL LATE. CHEERS.

When Jersey Avenue hits Easton Avenue they turn left and look for food. It is six in the evening. There are bars, dozens of neon lights illuminating restaurant windows and several empty parking lots in front of grocery stores.

"La Familia," Les reads.

"Pizza," Aaron says aloud in agreement.

"Seems premature,"

"What does?"

"New York is pizza city, right?"

"One of them anyway." They look at the sign again and then at their other options: Thai food, hot dogs and two other pizzerias.

"I guess pizza is big in Jersey too," Aaron says peering down Easton.

Les shrugs. "La Familia it is."

"I wonder if Rick even told his roommates," Les says when they are riding again. He reads a sign that appears to say something about an edible forest garden within a park. The sun has begun to set and the park has tiny rays of light inside. It is deep, dismal and calm, like the ocean at night.

"Me too. That'd be funny if we just showed up and lay out on the porch."

"I don't even care at this point. I just need somewhere to lay and be able to wake up. Dude, I'm going to New York tomorrow."

Rick's house is a small Victorian with chipped paint and an orange light above the front door. There is a porch swing with torn upholstery.

"Is this it?" Aaron says.

Les pushes his bike up along the side of the property and peers into the backyard.

"Well, I see a tent."

Aaron looks too. It is on its side, as though it has been blown over.

They knock on the front door and a girl answers. She is short and pale with curly brown hair.

"Hi, is Rick home?" Les says.

She shakes her head and looks out at their bikes. Then she nods. "Come on in. I don't know when he'll be home, but he mentioned you guys."

The house is dark. There are two couches with mismatched throw pillows. There is a light on at the back of the house and they follow the girl toward it.

"Want some water?" she says, picking up a knife and slicing the skins off a bowl of potatoes.

"No," Aaron says, holding up his water bottle. "I'm good. Great house." He looks around the kitchen.

"Thanks," she says. "So, I don't officially live here. But Rick lets me crash. I try to keep the place clean." Her tone is somber. The only noise is her cutting into the potatoes and faint traffic from the street outside. The house seems otherwise vacant.

"So, is that us?" Les points into the backyard.

"You can if you want. Or you can just sleep on the couches or whatever in the living room.

Nobody here cares."

"Okay," he says. "Deal," he smirks and folds his arms while looking around the kitchen for himself. "Are you having people over?" He motions at the potatoes.

"We're having a party tonight."

"Oh yeah?" Aaron says.

She nods and looks at each of them. "Sorry, don't mean to scare you. You guys are probably tired. It's going to be a beautiful night so we were planning to hang out on the porch anyway. Of course, you guys are more than welcome to join us."

"Thanks," Les says. "Honestly, we're on our very last night of our trip. I think we'll just crash and head out early."

"Yeah, thanks."

"Alright, well, I'm going to get settled," Les says.

"Me too. Thanks again," Aaron says.

She smiles shortly and waves with the knife in her hand.

The bathroom is crowded with towels and toiletries. They take turns showering, and afterward, when they see the girl leave they explore the house. There is a deep basement where they find a few old bikes leaning against the wall next to a bunch of opened boxes.

They don't go upstairs. Instead, they sit in the living room. They update the blog and scroll through pictures from the day. They roll out the sleeping bags and put their luggage near their heads. Aaron downloads "Eye of the Tiger" and uploads their Rocky and Mickey video onto his computer. He layers the song over the video and shows Les, who looks amused but stares intently at a book, anxious and rigid, which is rare for Les.

"One more dawn, one more day," Aaron says, closing the computer.

"This is it."

"Yeah."

To the best of their knowledge, Rick never comes home. At two in the morning, Aaron is startled awake by the sound of someone yelling out on the porch, which is followed by several laughs. Weed is in the air. The only people who come inside are those using the bathroom. He listens to their conversations for a while. They are mocking a group of kids they saw at a concert. They are jeering about being depressed and one of them knocks several beer bottles over. The laughter continues.

Soon, Aaron falls back asleep.

THOUSAND DOLLAR TRADE

March 2008 — three months until departure

When my birthday came, I couldn't help but hope that my twenty-third year of life would simply result in mounds of birthday cash, especially in light of needing to accrue all I could to pay for the Surly.

Of course, it didn't.

Three days after my birthday I got a call from Carter. "You'll be able to pick up the bike by the beginning of April."

"So," I said, hesitantly. "How much do you think it'll be after taxes?"

"Can you do twelve?" he asked, meaning twelve hundred—meaning two hundred more than I'd originally said I could spend. Meaning even more debt on top of my already spoken for savings.

"Twelve hundred?" I said. "Yeah, sure. No problem, I'm sure that'll be fine." *No problem? I'm sure that'll be fine? Who am I?*

Carter sounded unaffected. "Okay, cool man. I'll call you as soon as she's ready."

For whatever reason, putting $1,200 onto a credit card felt insurmountably worse than $1,000. I spent the next two days neglecting to study for midterms and instead drawing up lists of things I could sell. At the top were: CDs, books, the Shogun and my iPod. The iPod was second generation, which would get me about fifty dollars. The Shogun might go for one hundred if I cleaned and tried to tune it. My books were mostly theology and ministry books that were marked up and dog-eared, and even if I did sell them all, I might have come up with seventy-five dollars. My CD collection was a decent size, and if I could sell its contents to the few remaining purists who hadn't converted to downloading MP3s, then I might have been able to make another $150. Even if everything sold, I still wasn't even halfway to paying for the bike.

Feeling defeated, I slouched down on my parent's living room couch and tried not to think about a looming 19 percent APR. That's when my dad came into the room and stood in the corner by the heater. He always stood by the heater, even during the summer, as if manning his post. He had his arms folded at his chest.

"So, Aaron, I had an idea," he said.

I looked over. "What's that," I said.

"For your trip," he said. "I know you're trying to raise money to buy that bike, and I had an idea about some money."

Growing up, my parents never had the means to cough up an allowance of free money to give to their kids. If my brothers and sister and I wanted money, we had to work for it.

"You have a job for me to do?" I said. I imagined he might have thought up a little work I could do around the house for fifty or a hundred bucks. I turned my body and was facing him.

His posture was steady, his gaze direct. "Think of it like a trade," he said.

"A trade?"

"Yep, for your Bug. It's been sitting in our driveway for about six months. It's only collecting dust and spiderwebs now, and I have a feeling you probably won't be doing anything with it any time soon."

Of course! I thought. The Bug! Over the years my lack of desire to give my Bug the mechanical attention that it needed garnered my Dad's frank description of it. It was somewhat out of order, and in needing to ride my bike everywhere to train for the trip over the last year, I'd brushed the Bug off like a pest on my shoulder.

"Well, you're probably right that I won't be doing anything with it," I said.

"How about this," he said. "I'll take it off your hands for a thousand."

I was stunned. *One-thousand dollars for that piece of crap?* "Dad, are you sure? I mean seriously now—"

"Sure," he said, still calm. "This way it's out of your hair and you'll have the money for your bike."

Again, I was stunned. I sat motionless, thinking up ways I could come up with the extra two hundred far easier than twelve hundred. I also then contemplated my dad's close attention to my needs.

"I can see what I can do to get it running again," he said. "Your brothers have been asking if we can get it working again anyway."

I sat up and tried to refrain from letting my excitement spill out of me. I wanted nothing more than to leap into the air. I stood and followed my dad into his office to work out the details. After I signed over the deed, he handed me a check. I stared at it for a few moments and couldn't believe it.

One Last Hitchhike

"I can't believe it," Les says, taking off his helmet and pacing the asphalt. He looks up at the bridge. "I can't, I can't, I can't. There's no way!"

"I know," Aaron says consolingly. He looks ahead and around. They can see Staten Island from where they stand. "Who would have thought?"

Les points at a sign. "There should be a way for people on bikes to get onto the island."

Unlike the bridge they took in Havre de Grace, in Maryland, when they were warned by the sweating cop, the Outerbridge Crossing that leaves New Jersey and drops into Staten Island is a brief uphill stretch with one open lane and no shoulder.

"We can't chance it this time," Les says. "We have to do it right. We are getting to New York today."

"We might have to. Unless we get someone to give us a ride."

They ride around the New Jersey side of the bridge several times, passing below it and looking for any kind of pedestrian crossing.

"Come on," Les says, and they ride back to a gas station parking lot.

"We need a truck, or a pickup," he says quickly. There is excitement in his eyes. Now, all of their experience hitchhiking is being put to a final test. He dismounts his bike and waits at the entrance of the gas station. He waves at every truck that comes in and asks if they can get a ride over.

An hour passes and Les has spoken to fifteen or sixteen trucks.

They'd left Rick's house in New Jersey at seven. After topping off their food at a grocery store, they all but sprinted east toward New York. They pretended to race and laughed as they barreled around stopped traffic leading to the bridge. The air was brisk and the sky was overcast, as on the first day of the tour.

"Excuse me, no, no, no, don't do this," says a man from the concession stand at the gas station. He has walked over to talk to Aaron.

"I'm sorry," Aaron says turning around and approaching the man.

He points at Les and says, "Don't do this," and he wags his finger across the motorists fueling up.

"Sorry, sir, we just need to get to Staten Island. We have no way." Aaron can see how little of an impact his words are having with the man.

"I do not care," he says.

"Sir, is there any way for two guys on bikes to get across? Do you have any ideas?"

The man's face looks flustered and he peers over at their bikes.

"I'll buy something," Aaron says.

The man looks at Aaron again. "Okay, okay. Fine, fine. No bus here. If you buy, then fine."

Aaron follows him inside and pulls a Gatorade out of a refrigerator. When he says thank you the man grunts and picks up a newspaper.

"I got one," Les says peering into the store. "Come on!"

A silver Dodge pickup is waiting near their bikes. They drop his tailgate and help each other lift their bikes onto the bed. They close it and jump inside.

"Thank you, sir, we really appreciate it."

"Hey, don't mention it," says the man. There is a girl in the passenger seat with a backpack. She could be in high school and she is staring at her phone. The man is wearing a navy-blue NYFD T-shirt. He looks like a fireman, and he doesn't say anything as they cross the the bridge. Aaron offers to pay him but he shakes his head.

When they pull their bikes out of his truck and shut the tailgate he waves from out the window and pulls away.

"Scarce, but I'll take it," Les says, throwing his leg over his bike and pushing into the street. "Now let's go to Manhattan!"

LEARNING TO RIDE

April 2008 — two months until departure

After I'd paid for and picked up my brand-new Surly from Carter at the bike shop, I went home and rode it around my parent's neighborhood. It sparkled like a steel diamond under the sun. It had polished chrome components, a solid aqua steel fork holding my front tire in place and a perfectly matching aqua steel frame. Compared to the Shogun, it made riding over bumps and cracks in the road like rolling around in a Cadillac. Riding across America on it would be like floating on a pillow.

After riding around the block and nearing my parent's home again, I gently pulled my new brake levers and stopped two houses early. I put my foot on the ground and looked at the old sidewalk. As far as I could remember it had been the same cement for twenty years. I knew its cracks well. I'd spent years of my childhood scouring its crevices for ants, pennies and other artifacts. I'd played pogs with Henry Martinez on it, and I'd traded Star Wars cards on it with my friend William. I'd had the All-FOUR-One gang over to my house numerous times, and we'd walked away trying to look tough on it. I remembered where, on that very cement, my cousin Kevin and I would draw and cut out black cardboard cats with a pasted-on circular piece of aluminum foil for an eye, and how we'd set up what he called "cardboard kitties" in the street and wait for cars to drive up and stop before them. We always got a kick out of that.

Then I remembered the Christmas that I got my first bike, a purple Huffy with neon green handgrips and black paint splattering. My dad had noticed how I'd set it up in the corner of living room and stared at it, studying its immaculate specifications. He was pretty good at noticing the things that mattered to me. He'd asked me if I wanted to learn to ride it and I looked back at him and said I did.

From the front lawn, my mom held a camera in one hand and kept my baby brothers close with her other. My dad gave me directions: "Alright, Aaron, keep both hands on the handlebar and don't let it go. Put one foot on the right pedal. Don't worry, I've got you from behind."

I remember this scene today like something from an old, scratchy black-and-white film:

Father keeps his hand on son's back while son begins to inch forward. With more momentum son tries to steady the bike but sees it wobble and gets scared. Father is guiding him by holding his son's shoulder. Son puts his foot down and says he doesn't know how to do it. Father is encouraging, saying, "It's alright, it takes time. Trust me, it takes time. Let's keep going." Son begins to pedal again, each revolution without stopping feels like a new victory. Father is now jogging behind son saying, "Keep it steady; aim for the middle of the sidewalk." Mother aims camera and captures the moment her son unknowingly pedals down the sidewalk by himself, Father jogging close behind. Son stops in a patch of grass and looks back at Father. "I did it!" he exclaims. "I rode! I rode!"

NYC

After being dropped off, they ride south to where Pleasant Plains Avenue becomes Amboy Road. They turn left for Amboy and start up a clean, tree-covered bike lane.

On the map, Staten Island looks small compared to Long Island and Manhattan. As they ride they expect that every corner might drop them out upon the ferry terminal of the Hudson River's Upper Bay. But none do, at least not for nearly fifteen miles. When they do arrive at a new bike lane that hugs the southeasternmost shore of Staten Island, Les raises his arm and points at the water. "This is a New York coast; we are so close!"

It's not a shore that builds up and crashes like those in California. Instead, it pushes up and recedes gently, like river water. Its sands aren't golden and soft, and there are certainly no people out tanning. Aaron remembers the send-off ceremony in Huntington Beach and figures there likely won't be a beach in Manhattan to complete their tire-dipping ceremony.

When they do round their final bend they cease pedaling and peer up at the sky. In the middle of the Hudson Bay they see the Statue of Liberty. She is greener than expected, and the overcast sky makes everything about her features hard to distinguish. But she is there, motionless and emblematic. Beyond her is Ellis Island, and directly to the left is Jersey City. To the right is Governor's Island and the western edge of Brooklyn. But all is noise and clutter compared to the city, which is opened up before them, towering well above everything surrounding it.

"Going across?" A man at the ferry terminal says. He is working a booth and motions at an area with a stencil of a bike and a sign that reads:

BICYCLE WAITING AREA

Aaron takes a picture of Les who, despite his excitement, looks calm and ready to retire. From the waiting area, they continue to peer upon the skyline. Just as cowboys who've made their way across desert and plains, through forests and town, they've finally arrived at the big city. They know nothing of the buildings, nothing of the historic streets and nothing of the kind of people who live and work within it. They know New York in no other way but from movies, plays and books, and by talking to people about it all along their way. They have been like eager explorers, a reverse Lewis and Clark, with no way to know what their destination would actually feel and look like.

The ferry arrives and docks, and a stout man with a short beard opens a small gate and waves them over. As they board they feel the water somewhere deep beneath their feet. It makes the ferry sway. Aaron sits on one side of the waiting area and Les the other. There are no other people around to board and before long they hear the engine start up and feel the boat moving forward.

"I can't believe this," Aaron says. The engine is too loud, however, but seeing him speaking, Les moves over. "Come on." Aaron motions with his hand as he gets up and walks out of the passenger area toward the railing at the front of the boat. There are a dozen boats upon the Hudson, some coming up from the Upper Bay to dock in Brooklyn, and some drifting north along Manhattan's West Side. The water is choppy and white at its tips. They watch the Statue of Liberty pass on their left. As they approach the ferry terminal near Battery Park, Aaron turns to Les.

He puts a hand on his shoulder. He feels at a loss for what to say. He thought touring for this many weeks across the country would have garnered him something inspirational, something powerful. Les is looking him in the eye.

"Thank you," Aaron says.

Les smiles and snaps his fingers, just as he'd done a year ago at the coffee shop on the night they'd agreed to take the ride. He folds his arms and breathes in deeply and lets the air leave his body simply and says, "Any time."

Upon exiting the ferry, Aaron looks for a beach or a shoreline of any kind. Les follows close behind. It feels ridiculous to be looking for a place to dip their front tires at the bottommost edge of the city, especially since Battery Park doesn't appear to have a shore but more of concrete barrier that drops straight down into the water. After a few minutes of peering over several railings they give up. The excitement of finally being in the city is too overwhelming.

"I think we can postpone this," Aaron says. "I'm mean we're in New York after all. We should be relaxing and celebrating, right?"

Les nods and looks around. He looks sedated.

"You alright?

He nods. "Just taking it in."

"What do we we do now?"

It occurs to both that they hadn't thought of what they'd do as soon as they'd arrived. For forty days they had plenty to do. Life was lived by the mantra "eat, sleep and ride." But now, they have arrived. Now, there is little more riding that they need to do.

"Hungry?" Les says.

"Sure."

They head north slowly up Broad Street and stop to eat at a sandwich shop on the corner of Stone Street.

After lunch they decide to explore. Weaving over to Church Street, they learn quickly how to ride a bike in New York by watching other cyclists. There appear to be two rules: don't wear spandex, and don't stop ever, not even for pedestrians. Aaron makes the mistake of slowing at a red light and barely avoids being hit by a rider coming from behind.

From Liberty and Church they can see signs for ground zero. There are men deep in the earth working with cranes and tractors, and there is a wide, green fence that partitions the site from the pedestrian eye. Like a chasm, the site is gaping. It is awkward looking when contrasted with all other street corners around it that are full and filled with concrete and buildings. Hundreds of feet into the air are they, except for here.

They spend a couple hours reading and updating the blog at Café Angelique at Bleecker and Broadway, two blocks away from NYU. Les responds to friends' comments and e-mails, and on the main page of the blog he writes:

!!!!!!!! WE ARE IN NEW YORK !!!!!!

Outside, Aaron calls home and Les takes a picture of him holding his arms up in celebration.

July 22, 2008

Everybody thinks they know what it might feel like to walk the streets of Lower Manhattan because of the movies, but only those who live and move amongst it everyday could really explain how its buildings make walls that completely keep the sun from shining into it.

There are bikes locked to everything: trees, chain-link fences, fire hydrants, street signs. There are even bikes upside down and locked into trees seven and eight feet off the ground.

Millions of people call Manhattan home. Grime-colored sidewalks, never-ending noise and cars lined up for miles at stop lights show it. There are eyes everywhere; nothing goes unnoticed, and yet, in a city so full of people, it feels hard to be unique.

Still, we're just two guys on the road figuring things out and having a great adventure.

Bleecker merges into East First Street, and that merges with Houston right around the area that a nice-sized bike lane appears. They turn north again up Loisaida and left again at Fourteenth Street, which is not a very bike-friendly street, so they turn right up Third Avenue. From there they practice riding like New Yorkers. Aaron tears around a taxicab and cuts between two cars and Les yells: "WOOOO!"

Epilogue

In case you're wondering, we did end up dipping our front tires into the Atlantic and symbolically completing our coast-to-coast excursion. But it wasn't until our fourth day in the city. Why did it take us so long? Well, this would be a great opportunity for a lesson on how sometimes in life formalities fall by the wayside, or about how rigidly sticking to a plan isn't always preferable, or possible, but I have neither. Instead, I have what Les and I believed to be a good enough excuse. That excuse was New York City.

Of course, by *New York City,* I mean that we had arrived at, rode our bikes through, ate exotic foods in, napped in and hiked around Central Park in and enjoyed free coffee refills at as many cheap diners as we could in New York City! The necessity of completing our trip by dipping our front tires in the Atlantic waned in its importance, and even though we'd thought about it the day we got in, after days two and three it didn't really come up. By the evening of day three I'd even come to think that completing the tire-dipping ceremony might not really mean anything. Much like how Les would say, "I don't need to tour across America this summer," challenging me to think of our trip more as an adventure and less as a strict bicycling tour; we both seemed to accept that this detail just wasn't as important and that eventually, if we really wanted to do it, we'd get around to it.

With that said, we did get around to it. On the morning of day four we found ourselves waking up in a vacated apartment on the West Side that used to belong to a Broadway actress and ex-girlfriend of our friend Paul's stepbrother (an even more bizarre connection than it sounds, trust me). She'd apparently just moved across town and didn't mind Les, Paul (who'd come up from Maryland to visit and celebrate with us) and me sleeping over as long as we'd lock the door behind us. To this day I'm not sure how Paul arranged for us to stay there that night. There was no food, electricity or running water, just bare hardwood flooring and a sixth-floor view of Central Park from West Ninety-Fourth and Central Park West. It was beautiful. And it was free.

When Les woke, he, Paul and I agreed that since we didn't have any plans for the day we'd ride the subway down to Coney Island so that we could eat at Nathan's Famous Hot Dogs and then, clutching our full stomachs, walk down to the water to dip our tires.

That July morning was like every morning we'd seen so far in New York: overcast and slightly humid. The one thing it wasn't, though, was loud. Along the way to New York I'd grown to anticipate a rowdy, bustling city full of lights and chaos at all hours of the day and night. There were certainly parts of Manhattan that were bright and loud, but to me the city that never sleeps felt more like the city that might always be half asleep. Or the city that's tired of staying up. Whichever, that morning was nominally clamorous at best—I think I heard a few taxis honk from the street below. But this relatively peaceful setting seemed to fit with our decision to not dip our tires until we were almost ready to fly home.

We exited our subway car at the Coney Island-Stillwell Avenue stop and walked down Stillwell, stopping off at Nathan's for a hot dog and a picture, and then meandered through Coney Island tourists down to the boardwalk. Fortunately, Paul was with us. Without him we would have had a hard time taking pictures of the dipping ceremony. Hoisting our bikes onto our shoulders and beginning to trudge through the sand, the whole moment felt somber and surreal, like walking away from a best friend after dropping them off at the airport.

As my feet sank into sand with every step, and as the sound of gentle water approached and receded upon the nearing shoreline, the closer we came, the more dismal I was becoming. I was remembering the days of riding around Orange Country by myself and learning to love the bicycle while praying. I was remembering the planning and strategizing that Les and I did in preparation for the tour. I was remembering all the risks we took and the ways we challenged ourselves to be the types of men we'd wanted to be, and of course, I was remembering the friends we'd made while riding across America. I didn't want any of it to be over, but that's when I knew that completing the tire-dipping ceremony really did mean something.

It meant the end of something really good. The ride across the country was about looking for God with new eyes and having genuine adventures with one of my best friends. But the year before it, when I lost my girlfriend and best friend but learned through therapy about self-worth and the importance of close friendships, was about healing and being restored for my life's journey again.

As we walked into ankle-deep water, the cool, East-Coast ocean rolling up to greet me, I knew I wasn't going to simply feel ready to finish the trip and go home. I knew there'd always be a part of me longing for the summer of 2008 again. But I also knew how much completing this chapter in my life would mean to me later.

So, just as in California, in unison Les and I counted:

One—

Two—

Three.

We hoisted our bikes into the air and tipped them forward, dipping our front wheels into the sea. Paul snapped several pictures and we shrugged, just like dipping into the Pacific, and before we knew it, we were walking back toward the boardwalk.

A time to look for God and purpose with new eyes, I thought as I walked.

And indeed it was.

Aaron and Les
Coney Island, July 2008

Acknowledgments

In addition to dedicating this book to them, I also want to express my sincerest gratitude to the men who selflessly got me through a really rough chapter in my life. Jared, as I mention in the book, at the point in time that this story is set we didn't know each other as well as we do today. But that never mattered to you, did it? You chose to pick me up anyway, just as you've gone on to do several times since then. How could I express my thankfulness enough? Eric, who would have thought a simple trip to SLO could have meant so much to my life? Secretly, I think you might have known, you've always been really perceptive. Thanks for looking into my life and deciding to lead me. Tyler, your compassion exceeds your knowing, and you give of your time and resources with more abandon than anyone I've ever known. You are crazy love, and it's intoxicating. Les, you might be the person I am most indebted to, and in reading this I know you will say, *No way, just receive it.* Not only did you ride with me, live with me, fight with me and learn about becoming victorious with me, but you were the single greatest proponent of this book being written. You'll be an inspiration to me forever. Thank you.

Thank you, Katie Atkins, for being my general editor and making this book into something actually readable. Thank you Katrina Thomas, Karen Green, Jason Slavin, Joel Poindexter and Rachel Kirven for being my beta readers. Thank you Thomas Kirven for being my project manager. Thank you Aaron Delani for your artistic eye, for building my website and helping me do most everything technology-related with this book. Thank you Shane Kalai for shooting and putting together a knock-out Kickstarter campaign video. Thank you to my instructor, Justin Hocking, and my cohort, Dara, Tessa, Desiree, Erin, Grace, Gavin and Kali at the Independent Publishing Resource Center, for investing your time, thoughts and invaluable critiques on the beginning sections of this book.

Thank you, Ash, for believing in this project, for reading it and giving me honest feedback, and for being such an encouragement to me and my writing from the very beginning. Thank you, Dad, for letting me write about our story. Thank you, Joe Anfuso, for encouraging me to not be afraid to shelve the book in pursuit of discovering something deeper about myself in the process.

I have elected to change the names of characters in this story for their confidentiality, but I will always be indebted to everyone Les and I interacted with. Without them we wouldn't have known how possible it is for two touring cyclists to become "like sons" to strangers. For all whom we met and/or hosted us, if you've stumbled upon this book and remember Les and me somehow, thank you.

This book's manuscript was written in Brea, California, from The Coffee Bean and Tea Leaf, Starbucks on Brea Blvd. and Imperial Hwy., my parent's house and my desk at "the bank" while I was "at work"; in Fullerton, California, from the Whiting House, the Green Bliss café and the Night Owl; in Los Angeles at Novel Café, Stories Books and Cafe, the LOVE NAIL TREE Warehaas and "the Abbey" at apartment 401; during a flight from Burlington back to Los Angeles after visiting my friends Drew and Brittany on their farm; in Portland, Oregon, from the IPRC, Coffee Division, all the Stumptowns, Powell's on Burnside, the Albina Press and my desk at the Brooklyn Quarters.

In case you're curious, here's a short list of music that may have influenced the writing of this book: Cold War Kids: *Robbers and Cowards, Loyalty to Loyalty, Behave Yourself EP, Mine Is Yours*. Feist: *The Reminder*. Admiral Fallow: *Boots Met My Face*. Beach House: *Teen Dream*. Bon Iver: *For Emma, Forever Ago, Blood Bank, Bon Iver*. Byron Tomes: *"This Is Why We Ride."* Broken Social Scene: *Bee Hives, You Forgot It in People, Broken Social Scene*. Delta Spirit: *Ode to Sunshine, History from Below*. Explosions in the Sky: *The Earth Is Not a Cold Dead Place*. Joe Pug: *Messenger, Nation of Heat EP, In the Meantime EP, Live at Chapel Hill 4/11/11*. Josh Garrels: *Love & War & the Sea In Between*. La De Les: *Carlo*. Lambchop: *Mr. M*. Lost in the Trees: *A Church That Fits Our Needs*. MewithoutYou: *Brother, Sister*.

And here are the books: *Blue Like Jazz, Searching for God Knows What* and *A Million Miles in a Thousand Years* by Donald Miller. *The Writing Life* by Annie Dillard. *Making Shapely Fiction* by Jerome Stern. *The Complete Stories, Mystery and Manners* by Flannery O'Connor. *Bird by Bird* by Anne Lamott. *You Shall Know Our Velocity!* by Dave Eggers. *The Road* by Cormac McCarthy. *East of Eden* by John Steinbeck. *The Great Floodgates of the Wonderworld* by Justin Hocking. *Notes from the Tilt-A-Whirl* by N.D. Wilson.

Lastly, thank you. This is my first book, and it's always been one of my biggest dreams to write one. It means a lot that you'd find yourself reading it. Let's hang out and ride bikes some time.

About the Author

Aaron M. Green decided to add the letter "M" to his author name because when you Google "Aaron Green" you might be confused to find that he is currently a football player from San Antonio playing for Texas Christian University.

This Aaron lives in Southeast Portland with his dog, Jack. He enjoys bicycling, reading and road trips with friends. In addition to riding a bicycle across America, Aaron has been a bike mechanic, a banker, a warehouse manager, a coffee-maker, a seminarian, and a reporter on bicycle culture. Since 2011 he's been a writer and editor for LOVE NAIL TREE. In the distant future he wants to build a house.